About the Author

Martha Twine was born in London in 1948. She moved to Surrey in 1956. Educated at Guildford County School, she worked for over forty years in the public sector, mainly in London and the north east, during which time she gained an accountancy qualification, and worked in finance. She is now retired and lives in Haslemere, where she enjoys gardening and singing in local choirs.

Beyond Terror's Reach

Martha Twine

Beyond Terror's Reach

Olympia Publishers
London

www.olympiapublishers.com
OLYMPIA PAPERBACK EDITION

A CIP catalogue record for this title is
available from the British Library.

ISBN: 978-1-80074-060-0

This is a work of fiction.
Names, characters, places and incidents originate from the writer's
imagination. Any resemblance to actual persons, living or dead, is
purely coincidental.

First Published in 2021

Olympia Publishers
Tallis House
2 Tallis Street
London
EC4Y 0AB

Printed in Great Britain

INTRODUCTION

Hi! Ever wanted to know what really goes on in space? This book will tell you.

Some years ago, I was targeted by terrorists — an international collaboration of Islamic State, IRA and North American Mafia. They used electromagnetic technologies as weapons in their covert war on the Western World. Unexpectedly, long-term exposure to these technologies enabled me to navigate the electromagnetic environment, and unlock the secrets of space travel.

I am not the first to make these discoveries. Scientists, including the US military, have been using these technologies since the 19th century. As we travel into deep space, we meet people from Earth, living on different planets. They all arrived during the 20th century, mainly since the 1960s. Almost all of them came via the United States, and none of them used rockets to get there. There are also people not from Earth, with their own civilisations.

The planets we visit include tropical paradises and unpolluted natural worlds. But there is a darker side as well. Prepare to meet space cowboys and space pirates, space traffickers and villains. We barge into the middle of a major interplanetary war, and there is an attempt to take over the leadership of the US, by stealth from off-planet. So, it's not so different from Earth after all!

In the electromagnetic environment, you can create things just by using thought. This does not work well on Earth. But once you get outside the Earth's magnetic field, almost everything is possible. We go outside the universe, and get a glimpse of 'higher realms,' but at other times, we end up staring into hell. We also go back in time to the age of the dinosaurs, and forward, into the near future.

I am not a scientist, and may not always use the right words, but I have tried to tell it like it is — and here is the key. The same electromagnetic technologies that are exploited by criminals and terrorists for illicit purposes on Earth, are used by the military for advanced space travel.

We all know about 'beaming-up.' Well, you don't have to be in space to do that, and criminals have been doing it illicitly on Earth for years. These technologies are highly classified. That is why there is unwillingness to deal openly with criminal abuse of such activities on Earth.

Life, as lived on Earth, is just a tiny part of what humans are capable of. There are planets where there is no suffering, illness or poverty. What makes life worth living, and what really matters to human beings, remains the same, whether you are in a distant galaxy or on a space station near Earth. If this ever happens to you, it will be a life-changing experience. So, are you ready to take this trip? Good luck on your journey!

Martha Twine, 31 August 2020

THE HIDDEN GATEWAY

Brandon walked out of Edmonton bus station and across the car park. He was looking for a Caucasian, five-foot nine, wearing a black, flat cap, standing by a silver Toyota saloon, answering to the name of Connor. He caught sight of a man who fitted that description, near the exit to the car park.

'You Connor?'

'Yeah. And you must be Brandon.'

'Right. Good to see you,' Brandon replied.

'OK, Brandon,' said Connor, handing over a pair of sunglasses in a plastic bag. 'Now, here's what you have to do. You see that road going up the hill? Walk up there. The first shop is a newsagent's. Just before you get there, you make a left into the alley. Then you walk twenty steps and put on the glasses. Look for a set of stairs, go down, and you're on your way..'

There was a silence. 'Everything, OK?' asked Connor.

'Uh, yeah, I guess so,' muttered Brandon.

He took the glasses out of the plastic bag and tried them on.

'Hey man, why did they give us these cheap shades? I can't see a thing,' he protested.

'Look,' said Connor, 'I'll wait five minutes. If you get lost you can come back. I'll be in the car.'

Connor got into the car and closed the door. Brandon

turned and walked up the hill. His mind went back to the night before, when he visited an address on the outskirts of town, given him by a fellow criminal he met when he was serving time 'inside'. He was ushered into a back room. A technician was sitting at a desk, working on his computer. He had unusual industrial goggles, pushed back over his head.

'Hi, sit down,' said the technician, pointing to the chair opposite. 'Can I have your name, please?'

'It's Brandon — Just Brandon.'

'OK.' The technician typed the name onto a form. 'Now I need you to look this way. Yes, that's fine.' There was a flash, and Brandon's photograph appeared next to his name on the form.

'Almost done now,' said the technician, taking what looked like a tiny air pump out of a drawer. He stood up, walked round behind Brandon, and placed the pump behind his right ear.

A moment later, Brandon was out of the room, his ear still buzzing from the sound of the device. The technician remained hunched over his desk, typing in the serial number of the microchip that now identified Brandon, wherever he went.

But now, Brandon could see the newsagents, and the entrance to the alley. He counted twenty paces, and casually putting his hand in his pocket, drew out the plastic glasses. With a quick look round, he put them on. For a moment he could see nothing, Then, as his eyes got used to the darkness, he saw a set of stone stairs leading downwards. He walked down the steps, and turned a corner.

Things got brighter. He could see a man wearing a transparent visor, standing by a gate. The man opened the gate and let him through. On the other side of the gate, was a blinding, white light. Brandon could not see what was behind it. He heard the gate lock behind him.

'Just walk through the light area,' said the man.

Brandon felt himself lift up, surrounded by white light. He floated through white clouds, and dimly saw armed men standing in the background, as he fell, feet first, through a huge metal funnel, and out into a reception area. He was aware of blue sky, clouds and sun, shining down. He was in a goods wagon on a moving train. He heard a voice say, 'Move out through the door please.'

There was a door in the wagon. Brandon opened it and found it led into another wagon. He walked through. There were three men sitting huddled on the floor, wearing shabby coats and hats. Brandon noticed that he had got a lot smaller, and that he was wearing the same gear as the men. He had been told that he would get protective clothing within the electromagnetic environment, but this was not what he expected.

Brandon climbed onto a box and looked out of the wagon. It was as if a curtain had been drawn back to let the sunlight in. He saw a panorama of snow-capped mountains, pine-clad hills and blue lakes below. Then he realised that the metal funnel that he came through was the funnel of a large steam engine, which was pulling twenty wagons behind it. But there was no steam coming from the engine, and it moved silently, with hardly a rattle or a roll.

Brandon knew he had entered the secret world of the covert electromagnetic environment that covered North America. It cloaked and interpenetrated the real world, like a different dimension, constructed by technical specialists who worked for the Californian wing of the US Mafia.

Grey shapes came flying out of the white clouds above him, and poured through the funnel of the steam engine. Three more men came through the door of the wagon and sat down. Brandon wondered if they were there for the same reason he was — a chance of a fresh start in life, where no one knew about his past, and the promise of a job in the States.

After two hours, the train pulled into Idaho. By now, every wagon was full. There were men of different sizes, some significantly taller than others, depending on their rank and status. It dawned on Brandon that he was one of the lower-ranking groups. Once again, he was at the bottom of the pile.

As the train stopped, a station announcement ordered all men to disembark, and gather with their groups, where their leaders would meet them, and take them to their workplaces. Brandon followed the rest of his group of forty men, all with similar uniforms, to a space on the station where a tall woman in a long frock, holding a clipboard was standing.

The woman was in fact a male supervisor, wearing the uniform of ultrasound staff. Ultrasound staff did not carry weapons officially, and were not expected to take part in combat. They wore dresses to distinguish them from weapons-group staff, and to protect themselves from friendly fire on the battlefield. They managed the personnel and business side of weapons group operations. Weapons-group staff, like Brandon, were destined for the frontline.

'This way, everyone,' ordered the supervisor.

All the men followed her into an electromagnetic room, where the microchips in their heads were checked with a barcode reader, and matched to the list on the clipboard. After that, they were told to settle down and wait for their weapons' training. An instructor would come and show them how to use their weapons, and explain what they had to do. Then they were to rest, as they were not due on the frontline 'til the next day.

Brandon thought of the years he had spent serving his sentence for a violent crime, and how he had dreamed about gaining his freedom. Now, he began to doubt if he would ever be free. He was right. No one who entered that hidden world, the way he did, ever got out again or regained their freedom.

WAR STARTS AGAIN

I was walking in my garden, when a voice on an ultrasound wavelength said, 'All right, men, activate the deep plunderer!'

Suddenly, a huge force was pulling me backwards, as if a ton weight had been attached to my lower back. Electromagnetic oscillators started pulling my feet in different directions, shifting a gravitational charge from one foot to another. But this 'deep plunderer' was a new type of attack, involving the insertion of a stronger magnetic force, designed to fire independently of the electromagnetic pulses of the oscillators.

'Let's see how you like that, Miss Strontium 90!' the voice continued.

I could tell that the perpetrators were close by. Other terrorists, in electromagnetic form, were holding electronic pointer weapons, which relayed the power of the perpetrators' weapons at close range towards me. The men in electromagnetic form, known as 'ghouls,' had been beamed into my environment from the US in specially-constructed electromagnetic architecture. The perpetrators relied on WiFi from a private commercial satellite to connect with each other.

At the same time, a group of low-level ultrasound troops, broadcasting from the States, were herded into position, to carry out vocal attacks and report back on what was happening to me. These troops were not skilled staff, and they had not been prepared for the frontline. They were whispering to each other.

'You go first.'

'No, I'm not on yet.'

'It's awful! I feel like a mushroom, kept in the dark and fed manure.'

'The people that I work for are blue tits.' *1

'I was told I didn't have to go on yet.'

But though they did not realise it, they were all 'on,' broadcasting live on the terrorists' international computer system. They had been forced into a room with a set of interconnected microphones, positioned in front of chairs. The microphone in front of each chair could be switched on or off individually from a control room outside, run by Californian technical support staff.

Where had they come from? The technicians operating heavy electromagnetic weapons came from the British Isles. They were hired and trained by members of the Irish Mafia, and lived locally.

Most of them were vulnerable people, who came from deprived communities — homeless centres, travellers, drug addicts, people from a nearby trailer park and ex-convicts from the criminal underworld.

The weapons-group Mafia and ultrasound staff could operate from anywhere in the world, same as people can telephone from anywhere in the world, but usually, they were from New York, New Hampshire and West Virginia. Overall, the majority of terrorists came from the North East of the States. The technical specialists, without whom none of this would have been possible, came from California.

I needed to deal with the perpetrators in the British Isles, who were operating electromagnetic weapons inside vans and behind garage doors within range of me. I also needed to remove their US weapons-group electromagnetic counterparts.

'Let all terrorists in the British Isles and the United States in existence, in all countries in existence, get what's coming to them!' I shouted, using a formula I had programmed into the ether earlier.

The electromagnetic environment can be programmed like a computer system, via voice, thought, or gut feelings, provided you make it clear where the programme begins and ends. As I spoke the formula, I connected to NATO's enhanced voice recognition systems in the ultrasound bandwidth. The NATO enhancement was a major step-change for me. It meant that all I had to do was repeat the form of words I had previously programmed into the ether, and all the perpetrators and their assistants died instantly.

Among the dead was a man called Brandon. As he died, the US Mafia computer system picked up his death, and recorded it on the staff list, against his microchip serial number. As arranged by my programme, the bodies of all the dead flew straight to a US military base in New York State, where they were recorded and destroyed.

At that moment, there was a noise like a fast jet plane just above me. I looked up and saw a small aircraft. It was white with a smooth, streamlined design like Concorde. It had amazing manoeuvrability, flying very low, and descending at the same time. It curved into a forty-five-degree turn, and headed for the terrorists' control centre, across the road and further down the valley on the other side.

The terrorists' electromagnetic weapons attack had alerted

the Royal Air Force. Under their terms of engagement, if they detect illicit activities above a certain electromagnetic strength, they send an aircraft. In this case, they sent a drone which looked and sounded like a jet plane, to melt the WIFI router of the terrorists' control room, disconnecting it from the internet. That temporarily stopped terrorists using powerful weapons equipment, because they needed WIFI to connect with the weapons operated by the US Mafia.

They also needed WIFI to connect with equipment in their nearest control room. That equipment included:

-   Infrared to 'find the body'.
-   Ultrasound to talk to each other, and to broadcast at me using synthetic telepathy. *2
-   A CD of my biodata, including chemical profiles of my sweat, saliva and hair, extracted by technical specialists, to enable their sensors to lock onto me.
-   Functional magnetic resonance imaging (fMRI) which measures brain activity, and which Mafia scientists have adapted to interpret what a person is seeing in their mind's eye.
-   EEG, used by Mafia scientists to diagnose what a person is feeling and thinking.

The RAF got rid of my attackers, but now I began to feel tired and drained. My eyes wanted to shut, and I went back into the house and slept for the rest of the day. The terrorists' weapons affected me quite seriously.

When I woke up, I tuned into the computer that runs the universe. *3 You need a reasonably strong electromagnetic charge to be able to do that, but I was swimming in the stuff all the time, because of the terrorist attacks. Once you extend your mental antenna into outer space, there is more than enough electromagnetic power in every subatomic particle there to achieve whatever you want.

'I need to understand where these attacks are coming from, and what type of equipment the perpetrators are using,' I said.

My mind cleared, and I found myself on the edge of a sandy desert, with red-rock mountains and weird rock bridges carved out by the wind, like those you find in Utah. I was looking across a flat, desert plane towards a huge city. The city was constructed out of transparent, reinforced glass. Tall skyscrapers and cone-shaped buildings competed for space with lower office blocks. Wide streets divided the buildings, but there was not a car in sight. All the cars were parked neatly outside the city on the desert sand. They were mainly sport utility vehicles — SUVs, and they clearly came from Earth.

'...came from Earth.'

As I spoke those words, it dawned on me that I was on another planet. The planet was called Igrashel. The city looked as if modern humans lived here, but the lack of cars made it seem eerie. As I watched, a white robot walked slowly down the road, patrolling the area. The robot looked like a man in white armour, seven feet tall. His movements were mechanical, and it was obvious that he was being controlled remotely.

Close by where I was standing, outside the city, there was a set of brick stairs, leading to an underground building. I willed myself to be invisible, and went inside. The underground room was spacious, with two levels. On the top level, there were rows of beds with men sleeping in them. On the level below, there was a workroom, with a wooden table and chairs, and a small kitchen.

Men wearing white, protective head masks, were making

18

drinks. The head masks, which shielded them from over-exposure to electromagnetic radiation, were made of skin tight white material that pulled over their heads, and zipped up at the back. You could see the men's features beneath the masks.

I recognised the men as coming from the US Mafia's Californian technical support staff. They were the people who made the difference between success and failure in the terrorists' operations, because they ran all the machinery and equipment which supported the terrorists' electromagnetic architecture and their more advanced weapons. Tuning into the universal computer system, I asked, 'Where are the weapons used to attack me?'

My view was directed out of the underground building, along a bank and up behind an old disused brick building. There, positioned on a set of metal cross supports, were an array of five oblong boxes containing electronic generators. The boxes whirred quietly.

'How could these do me any damage?' I thought.

I followed the electromagnetic trail from the boxes into space, and found a commercial space station, concealed by advanced stealth cover, located not far from Earth. The boxes were transmitting into a set of receivers which shone high-powered, pulsed, electronic beams down to Earth. The terrorists needed a strong power source for their enhanced electromagnetic attacks, and they knew they would be caught if they switched on an array of electrical generators on Earth, so they went off planet. Following the light rays, I found myself back in my garden.

'Right,' I thought, 'I'd better return to the scene of the crime to find out more.'

I went back to the underground room on Igrashel. A man

wearing a white lab coat, and carrying a shielding helmet, was sitting at the table in the kitchen, talking to one of the terrorist team.

'Things are not working as well as we hoped. She seems to be unaffected by the radiation.'

'What's the problem?' asked the technician.

'The magnetic components are supposed to amplify the impact of the oscillators and enhance the gravitational pull, but they are not powerful enough,' said the scientist.

'Can you increase the power?' asked the technician.

'Not really,' the scientist replied. 'Of course, we can double the intensity, if that's what you mean, but we would be picked up in two seconds by the British military. And the infrasound components would be instantly detected.'

'How are we to deal with her then?' asked the technician. The scientist shrugged his shoulders.

'Keep trying with these for now. The infrasound device may have an effect over time.'

I was not aware of any infrasound components, but if there were any, they were probably being used to try and demoralise me, by inducing fear and awe. I decided to talk to the US military about them. But first I had to stop the US Mafia targeting me from Igrashel.

I selected all the terrorists in the underground building, and created a powerful sonic tracking device on their heads, which would be audible to the city's robots. Then I sat back and waited. Soon, two large white lorries appeared, and several white robots got out. I could hear the voices of people on the intercom from the city's law enforcement centre directing them.

'It's coming from underground. Look for an underground

entrance.'

The robots searched around but could not find it. I appeared, and pointed to the steps leading to the underground hide-out.

'It's down there,' I said.

The robots turned their heads in the right direction, and advanced towards the steps. 'Right, now go down and enter the premises,' came the instruction over the intercom.

The robots slowly made their way down the stairs and broke open the doors. There was a lot of screaming as terrorists came running out. The robots picked them up, two at a time, under each arm, and put them in the back of the lorries. When they had cleared out the underground building, they drove off.

Next day, I visited the US Military electromagnetic border control centre in New York. That is where the US Military operate their patrols to prevent illegal entry into the country by people in electromagnetic form. I stood at the door, and a woman in military uniform appeared.

'Hi, can I talk to the officer on duty, please?' I asked.

The woman recognised me. I was a fairly regular visitor, often escorting groups of people rescued from the terrorists to the US entry portal.

'Oh, it's you, OK, come in,' said the woman officer.

We went into the guard room together. Several US border control staff were working in there. 'Oh hi, Martha,' said the duty officer. 'How can I help you?'

'The ghouls have started attacking me again,' I said, 'and according to their technicians, they are using infrasound components. Is that something you have an interest in?'

'Well, now,' said the duty officer, smiling, 'If it's infrasound, we certainly do have an interest. In fact, we are authorised to intervene in any illegal use of infrasound equipment.'

'Is there any difficulty if the illegal use is from outer space targeting the British Isles?' I asked.

'That I don't know,' said the duty officer. 'Leave it with me. We'd like to help if we can.'

'Thanks,' I said, and I left, hopeful that the matter was sorted.

But it wasn't. Nothing changed.

'It's probably due to the red tape that holds things up when more than one NATO country is involved,' I thought.

When I got home, a group of US Mafia ghouls, dressed in shabby black hats and coats were being let loose inside electromagnetic architecture, operating 'pointers' in my direction. They had been exposed to radiation which reduced them in size. In this mode, they could be transported to anywhere in the world. Terrorist technicians created the architecture, using 'copy' and 'paste' commands on their laptops. These commands activated equipment which worked like a 3D printer, using a fine web-like substance, that could be sprayed out of a machine, and which hardened into any shape required.

The pointers operated by the US Mafia were linked to heavy-duty oscillator equipment, being operated by British criminals inside the garage of a house that looked towards my garden. The men inside the garage wore black protective clothing, because of the powerful radiation coming from the equipment they operated. They were using large radiation beams, which penetrated the garage door easily. The beams acted as a delivery agent carrying electromagnetic pulses, designed to destabilise my body.

In my mind's eye, I searched for the source of the attack, picked up the men and eliminated them with the voice command:

'All terrorists in existence in the British Isles, take THAT!'

'THAT' was a word I had programmed into the NATO voice recognition systems. It caused the internal organs of terrorists to receive a strong, continuous electric shock, enough to kill them after a few minutes. As usual, once dead, the bodies of the terrorists went to the US military base in New York. That way, the US military could keep a count of the number of dead, and which countries they came from.

On the command 'THAT!,' men writhed and fell. Other men in miniaturised form, positioned along the electromagnetic architecture surrounding my house, fell to the ground as well. At that moment, a number of senior, ultrasound, mind-control terrorists, wearing female uniforms, appeared on a balcony. Like most ultrasound terrorists, they had a background of people-trafficking. They

gave orders for twenty men and women, who were victims they had kidnapped, to be downloaded into the arena that occupied my garden.

The victims had been kidnapped for ransom, but their families had been unable to pay up, and the people traffickers wanted me to kill them, so that the bodies would be automatically transferred to the US military, saving them the trouble of having to dispose of them. They hoped that I would annihilate everyone in sight, without looking too closely.

But I was looking closely.

'All people-traffickers in existence, take THAT!' I shouted.

The men in women's uniform fell off the balcony, screaming, leaving their victims sitting on the ground, their hands tied behind their backs.

'All victims in existence, go Green,' I said.

Going 'Green' gave people the cleverest brain in the universe, and perfect health of mind and body. If I used the Green command inside a terrorist environment on Earth, it also took people to the US electromagnetic border control centre in New York, where they arrived with wrist-bands stating where they came from.

The NATO voice recognition system picked up my command, and all the victims were whisked off to the US border control portal. They landed unsteadily, because they were still tied up. I joined them.

'All victims that went Green, untie now!' I announced.

The ropes fell from the victims, and the US border guards opened the doors and let them in. Three visiting Canadian policemen were in there too. They were taking a keen interest in what was going on.

'We think these victims may be Canadians,' said one of the police.

'We're just checking their wrist-bands now,' said a border guard. They inspected the victims' wrist-bands.

'Yes,' said the border guard, 'They are Canadian.' A senior Canadian policeman turned to me.

'Can you do another victims' call out?' he said. 'We think there are more Canadians that have just been brought into the terrorist arena from trucks outside.'

'So,' I thought, 'the authorities are monitoring the terrorists' activities remotely.'

'All victims not already selected, go Green now!' I

shouted.

There was a sudden rushing noise, and fifteen large sacks landed outside the US portal. The sacks were roughly human shaped, and looked rather ghastly.

'All victims go free and untie now!' I cried.

As the sacks came off, we could see the pitiable state of the poor men and women inside.

'The cowardly cunters!' muttered one of the Canadian police. 'I'd like to get my hands on them.'

'We all would,' said a US border guard, as he helped the victims up.

Now that they had gone Green, the victims all had perfect health of mind and body, so the urgency of the situation was over. I felt sorry for the US border control staff, who had to deal with whatever was thrown at them, twenty-four hours a day. It was much the same for me too, but at least I could go home and put my feet up.

But why had these attacks started again? As described in *Kiss Terror Goodbye*, when the North American Mafia, Irish Mafia and Islamic State teamed up to launch an electromagnetic war on Europe, they thought that they could force me to work on their side. But they found out they were wrong. Now they no longer had any illusions. They wanted to restart the war, using the British Isles as a jumping off point, and they saw my continuing existence as a barrier to achieving that. Their objective now was to get rid of me, whatever it took.

INTERGALACTIC SPACE STATION

The constant attacks from electromagnetic terrorists were once again becoming a regular feature of my life. I wanted a change. My visit to Planet Igrashel had re-kindled my taste for space travel, and the prospect of distant worlds and unknown star systems was attractive.

'I want to go to a different Galaxy!' I announced to the Universe.

Suddenly I was there! Bright red and yellow lights, colourful nebulae and glowing clouds of shining white matter, came into view, in a three-hundred-and-sixty-degree panorama. As my eyes got used to it, I could make out a huge gyroscope, slanted at an angle somewhat off ninety degrees. It was a giant wheel with a large spoke through the middle. The spoke had shorter spokes connecting to different parts of the wheel, and there were spherical nodes at the junctions.

Behind the gyroscope, and a long way off, was a large, pale yellow-grey gas giant. It did not emit its own light, but glowed in the distant light of a far-away star. Amidst all the lights, I thought I saw a charcoal-coloured object, the shape of a woodlouse, sneaking in on the left side of my vision.

'Not possible,' I thought.

But as I moved closer to the wheel, I saw lots of other woodlice, stationary, around the wheel's spokes. A long dark rope came down in front of me. I followed it down. At the end of it was a kind of basket, with a light over it, and inside the basket, was a mud-coloured human figure.

I had always thought it unlikely that non-Earth humans could exist in space. But there was this human figure. The basket with the light over it appeared to be an anchor. The human moved up out of the basket, using the rope to assist its progress. It wore an all-in-one outfit with a transparent visor over the eyes and nose, and had teddy-bear ears, enclosed within the suit. Other humans came walking through space towards the anchor, holding more ropes. They secured the anchor to part of the giant wheel and returned to access points on the wheel, where they re-entered it.

My attention moved to the charcoal-coloured woodlouse object. It had a matt finish, designed to absorb light, making it invisible to the eye from space.

'Oh! It's a scout ship!' I realised.

The door of the scout ship was open and connected to a flexible walkway leading to one of the spokes on the wheel. Inside, twenty brown-clothed humans were queuing to leave the ship. Its interior was brightly lit, and it looked more like a train carriage than a spacecraft, with rows of
comfortable airline seats all facing forward, and two sets of tables in the middle, with workstation facilities.

Inside the spokes of the giant wheel there were moving walkways packed with humans travelling downwards towards the centre. They had removed their headgear, to reveal that they had normal human heads. The teddy-bear ears on their space suits were receiver/transmitter headsets. They were all clean-shaven white males, standing about five-foot nine inches tall, with short, mid-brown hair. Other similar groups of men, wearing space suits, joined the lines of crew pouring down the walkways, through junction centres, on all sides.

The wheel was connected to a large space station below it, which provided changing rooms, rest rooms and a cafe. Inside, men were changing out of space gear, packing the gear into lockers, getting washed, and reappearing in dark trousers and maroon crew-necked jumpers. From there, they descended into a domed building with an upper balcony. The balcony overlooked the floor below, where there was a cafe with brown chairs and tables. Waiters were bringing beer in glasses on trays. The glasses bulged out in a circle, to mark where the top of the liquid should be, and went vertical again for another inch and a half to make room for foam on top.

The waiters were strikingly different. They were over six-foot tall and thin, with glamorous, shoulder-length feminine hair-dos, and their hair was mauve in colour. They were wearing a lot of eye make-up, with long lashes and eye-liner. They had ivory skin, and in profile their noses were retroussé, ending not in a point, but in a concave dimple above their nostrils, descending into a protruding mouth and chin. They wore mauve aprons that matched their hair.

So how did the astronaut commuters get from the space station to their planet? I found myself in a small aircraft like a Boeing 737. Rows of men were sitting in airline seats, while a mauve-haired waitress offered drinks. The shuttle aircraft did not move forward. Instead, it descended vertically until it reached the planet's atmosphere. Right at the top of the planet's atmosphere, there were docking stations, where the shuttle aircraft recharged their electrical motors. The passengers disembarked, and changed onto smaller aircraft, which took them to airports in different parts of their world, which was called Planet Zircon.

I decided to follow two charcoal-coloured scout ships to their mother ship. One of the scout ships held men in heavy space suits, designed for space walks on the outside of the mother ship. The other one carried crew wearing lightweight 'teddy-bear' helmets with headsets under their outer clothing. The mother ship loomed into sight. It was about half a mile long, with black matt, light-absorbing paint. There were fin-like protrusions along each side, each one capable of holding six docked scout ships.

The ship had clearly seen better days. No doubt maintaining it was a full-time job for the space walkers. Inside the ship, at one end, there was a small cafe and a billiard room, separated by a clouded glass partition, where crew members were occupying their time. In the middle of the ship, there were several commercial bars on different floors. The bars were heavily over-subscribed, so much so that the mauve-haired waiters had to carry their trays of drinks high in the air, to avoid hitting the heaving crowds of drinkers.

The central area had no scout ships docked outside. This was a good place for viewing the stars from the upper decks, which were kept dark for that purpose. In a spacious room at the front of the ship, the navigation team were leaning over tables with huge maps spread out on them. The pilot sat at the controls, while the co-pilot leaned back against a wall seat.

I left them to it. When I checked back, the ship was stationary and the navigation room was empty. The sky was pale indigo, with a moon, not quite full, on one side. Straight ahead was the massive, yellow gas planet, that I had seen before, and to the right, further down, was a planet in semi-darkness, with blue water surrounding a wide, uneven band of land that stretched from the North to South Pole. The Earth once looked like that, before tectonic plate movement created the continents, we are now familiar with.

It was getting darker, and I had missed the disembarking process. To judge from the position of the yellow gas giant, we were still not that far from Planet Zircon. I called to mind one of the men I saw drinking at the bars, and tuned into his frequency. Immediately I found myself in a light grey bedroom, with a double bed in it. The pillows and quilt were grey, and a young man about thirty years old, who I recognised from the bar, was lying there, fast asleep.

A woman came in carrying a beige melamine tray with sandwiches on it, and placed it on the bedside table. She was about five-foot seven, with white skin and dark shoulder-length hair in a style reminiscent of the young Queen Elizabeth II of England. She wore a long, sleeveless nightdress, with a tiny blue and white flower pattern, and frilled shoulder caps.

The woman pulled a grey blind down over the window, and went into a small, grey-walled kitchen next door. The kitchen was streamline, with grey fixtures and fittings and a metallic sink. As the woman made herself a cup of coffee, two children, a girl of six, with two mid-brown plaits, and a boy of four with fair hair, came into the kitchen. A man who looked Cantonese followed them. He was dressed in the same dark trousers and maroon crew-necked top as the astronauts had worn. His skin had a beige tone, and his short straight black hair was combed toward in a fringe. I had several men in the space station cafe who looked similar.

The woman offered the man a coffee. After drinking it, he left, followed by the children. He made his way along the main corridor of the building, passing the doors of several apartments on either side. Then he turned a corner, and climbed three stairs to his own home, which was a maisonette on two floors, at the end of the house. The man went into the living room and sat down in a large leather-look chair. The wall to his left had a low-level lighting feature, from which you could see a fitted seating ledge along the wall, with cushions embroidered with plants and flowers.

Another woman in a nightdress, similar to the first woman, brought the man some sandwiches on a tray. Then she went upstairs to the bathroom, removed her clothes, and began to give her toenails a cuticle treatment, before applying nail polish. She put cotton wool between each of her toes. Her husband came upstairs, and seeing her in a state of undress, began caressing her body.

Outside the house there was a white streetlight, which looked like a large inverted cup and saucer. On the other side of the road was another block of flats, like the one I had just left, made of a material that looked like beige sandstone. There were several of these buildings spaced out on either side of the road. A black taxi, which I identified as a 1940 Ford Standard, pulled up outside the house opposite, by the street lamp. A Cantonese man got out and went into the nearest building.

The night sky was overcast, with no stars visible. As I watched, a group of tiny, brown deer with many antlers moved past. A tall, thin fox with a pointed face, a white mask, vertical-pointing ears and a white tip to its tail hurried by. It was too dark to see anything else, so I decided to return during daylight hours.

FIRST CONTACT

Next morning, I took a look at the landscape surrounding the buildings I visited the night before. The land dropped steeply into a deep valley, with trees of light green, dark green and beige. In a clearing below, I saw a large deer about six feet high, trotting through woodland. Much further below, there were beige stone houses, bungalows and two-storey buildings, each with a defined garden of mown lawn and shrubs planted round it.

Next to the houses was a further education college. The second floor was divided into classrooms, where young Cantonese men sat with exercise books at melamine work tables, taking notes, while lecturers talked and wrote on white boards.

Downstairs there was a self-service restaurant. A long chill cabinet was placed diagonally across the room. Glass bowls containing salads and other colourful foods were standing in the cabinet, with large serving spoons and forks.

Further up the hill was a very large beige building. The ground floor was square, with high walls. Above the walls there was an octagonal tower, from which a spire like that of a church extended into the sky. Inside, there was a wood panelled reception area, leading into a vast hall, with an amphitheatre of dark brown wooden benches lined with dark leather upholstery. The hall was lit by tall glass panels in the octagonal tower.

In the middle of the amphitheatre, at the back, was a raised wooden platform. The benches were occupied by middle-aged men wearing brown and grey coats, debating with each other. A man wearing a black gown sat on the platform, directing what seemed to be a parliamentary process.

The speaker was having a hard time keeping order, as everyone was talking at once. More middle-aged men were sitting in wooden galleries above.

Along the main road below the hill, there were beige houses with gardens, a small red-brick church, and rows of shops. The glass shop fronts were reminiscent of the 1960s, displaying shoe repairs, women's underwear, household equipment and garden ornaments. All the buildings were surrounded by trees, giving the feel of a country town, rather than a capital city.

Many things about this world were similar to life on Earth, but not quite the same. How had this civilization arrived, and when? I wanted to ask questions, but who could answer them? I tuned in to get a hint on which building might be best, and found myself at the junction of several roads, with cars passing on all sides, and a canal in the background. One of the shops, which had a board over the front saying 'Tourist Information', attracted my attention, and adjusting my appearance to conform with local expectations, I went in.

A kind lady at the modest reception desk, whose name was Ardeana, asked if she could help me. 'Do you speak English?' I asked.

'Oh, yes,' replied Ardeana, 'We speak all languages here. We have the technology.' Ardeana pointed to a tiny device attached behind her ear.

'Are you a tourist?' she asked.

'Yes,' I said.

'If you would like to go up the stairs,' Ardeana said, 'someone will be able to help you.'

'Thank you,' I replied.

I went up the small creaky wooden staircase. At the top was a beige melamine door with a glass window in it. A man aged about thirty, with short dark hair slicked back in a side parting opened the door. He was of Caucasian appearance, wearing a light khaki short-sleeved shirt and trousers. His name was Sholouf. Inside, sitting at a table was one of those tall people with mauve hair, whose name was Adia.

'Hello,' said Adia. 'Please come in. How can I help you?'

I sat down opposite Adia, wondering where to begin.

'I'm a bit lost,' I murmured. 'I wonder if you could tell me what is the name of this place?'

"Where have you come from?' Adia asked, reassuringly.

'I'm from Earth,' I said.

Did you come on a space ship?' asked Adia.

I nodded. That wasn't exactly accurate, but my intuition warned me it would have to do for now. 'Ah,' s/he said. 'You need to go upstairs. Come with me.'

We went upstairs to a similar room, where another man with dark, slicked-back hair, was standing. 'This lady's from Earth,' said Adia, and s/he left.

The man, whose name was Arthurus, smiled. 'We are all from Earth originally,' he said.

'When did you come here?' I asked.

'I have lived here all my life,' said Arthurus. 'My mother and father are from the United States. What part of Earth are you from?'

'I'm from the British Isles,' I said.

'Oh, that is where we come from originally,' said Arthurus.

'Do you mean your parents came from the British Isles?' I asked.

'No, my parents are from the United States,' said Arthurus, 'but they came from the British Isles originally.'

'How did you get here?' I asked.

Arthurus gave me a confiding look, and I sensed that what he was telling me was personal information.

'My parents met on a space station outside Earth, thirty years ago,' he said. 'I was born from an external womb, and from there, I was brought to this planet. I am thirty years old.'

'Was that the same for everybody on this planet?' I asked.

'Yes,' said Arthurus.

'So,' I thought, 'chances are, most people here have been created using test-tube technology.'

At that moment two older gentleman appeared. They had come down from the floor above, and seemed to have senior status. They had been listening to our conversation.

The most senior man, whose name was Rufusha, asked, 'What year is it on your planet?'

"It is 2019,' I replied.

Rufusha gasped.

'That is the same date as here!'

'Are you aware that nobody on Earth knows of your existence?' I asked.

'No,' said Rufusha, looking surprised. 'I knew that our existence was somewhat "sub-judice" to start with, but I thought by now, everyone on Earth would know about us.'

It suddenly dawned on me that I was probably the first

alien from Earth that these people had ever met. Also, I was talking to aliens for the first time. They looked like us, but I could tell that their planetary memory and culture were not the same.

It is hard to explain how I felt at that moment. Things had got a lot stranger than I was expecting. I just couldn't match what was happening with my expectations about humans in space. Until recently, I didn't believe there were any. I just wanted to get away. So I thanked Rufusha and Arthurus for their assistance and said it was time for me to go.

'So soon?' asked Rufusha in a kindly manner. 'Do please come back again if there is anything else you want to ask.'

I began going down the stairs. My head was going fuzzy as I started to absorb the implications of what had occurred. I was not the only one in shock. As I passed the door on the first floor, I looked in. Adia was shaking in her chair, and Ardeana and Sholouf were trying to calm her. People from Earth had never walked in unannounced asking for tourist advice before, and Adia was not prepared for it. I went over to Adia and sent her an energy beam. Adia stopped shaking, and sat up.

'I'm all right now,' she said.

'I think you should go home and rest,' said Rufusha, who had joined us. Ardeana ordered a taxi, and Adia went home.

Sholouf said, 'That light beam I saw… do you do healing?'

"Well, it can help,' I said.

'Excuse me,' said Sholouf, and he lit a cigarette.

I noticed his hand was shaking, so I quickly sent him an energy beam as well.

'Ah, that's better,' sighed Sholouf, and he stopped shaking. 'I feel much better,' he added. 'Really, I feel better than usual.'

'I ought to go now,' I said, and left.

As I went outside, I caught sight of Adia in a black car like the one I had seen under the streetlamp the night before. Invisibly, I joined her in the taxi, to make sure s/he was OK.

'Don't worry,' said the taxi driver, 'I'll make sure you get home all right.'

Afterwards, I checked up on Adia's progress. She was at home, sitting up in bed, speaking on an old-fashioned 'walky-talky' mobile phone to her office.

'I'm fine now. In fact, I feel even better than I normally do. Please don't worry about me.'

That night, I started thinking about Arthurus, and wondering if he might be in shock as well. I decided to go back and check. Arthurus was still in his office. He was lying back in an easy chair, and Ardeana was giving him a cup of coffee. He was still slightly in shock. Immediately, I sent him an energy beam. Then I noticed Rufusha standing there.

'Ah,' he said, 'I was hoping you would come back. I wanted to ask you about how you arrived here. Did you come on a spaceship, or did you come on your own steam, as it were?'

'On my own steam,' I said.

'I thought so,' said Rufusha. 'How did you find out how to do that?'

'It happened because of war on our planet,' I said. 'I was attacked, and through that experience, discovered how to navigate in electromagnetic environments.'

'Ah yes,' said Rufusha, 'we use them in our space technologies, for example in vertical descent and take off.'

Rufusha's words reminded me of the vertical descent from

the space station to planet Zircon, and the force-field at the top of the planet's atmosphere.

'You have healing technologies,' continued Rufusha, with an interested look.

'Yes,' I said. 'Would you like to have complete health of mind and body, the cleverest brain in the universe, and the ability to pass it on to others?'

Everyone in the room said 'yes' together. So I selected everyone in the building and sent them Green energy.

There was silence for a moment, as everyone took in what that felt like, and began thinking from a completely different place. I would like to have the same experience, but though I can arrange it for other people, I can't give it to myself. So now I was definitely the dumbest person in the room.

'Excuse me a moment,' said Rufusha, and he went out.

'I know where he's gone,' said Arthurus. 'He wants to help a friend of his who has been suffering from bouts of truculence and sadness.'

'I expect he means depression,' I thought.

Suddenly, the door was thrown open, and a man in his forties suddenly appeared. He did a backflip into the room, ending standing up, his arms outstretched.

'I'm all right again! I'm all right again!' he shouted.

Rufusha came in behind him, smiling. Then he vanished into thin air. I picked up that he had gone to help a relative. He reappeared after a few minutes, looking very happy.

'Is there anything else that you could pass on to us?' he asked.

'Well,' I said, 'on my planet, I passed on all the abilities that I had learned from navigating the electromagnetic environment to everyone on my planet who wished to use them, with the provision that these abilities could only be used for helpful purposes. Would you like me to pass that on to you, or to your whole planet?'

There was some conferring about this. Arthurus said, 'We are always being told that we need to make faster progress on our world. Wouldn't this help us?'

In the end, Rufusha announced, 'We think it would be better if you just pass your abilities on to us first. We will be able to consult with our authorities, and if they wish, we can pass the abilities on to our whole planet.'

So that was what happened. It was time to go, but before I left, I asked Rufusha the name of his planet.

'Our planet is called "Atman",' he said.

The name was surprising, so I asked him to spell it out. According to Wikipedia, 'Atman' means 'inner self, spirit or soul' in Sanskrit.

'We were given the name by the United States, when we first arrived in the 1960s,' Rufusha said.

I accepted that Americans had arrived on Planet Atman in the 1960s, but I suspected Rufusha had been around in space on other planets earlier on, and also, that he had been born and educated in the UK. Why? Because of the way he talked. Being from the UK myself, I thought he sounded like an Oxbridge graduate. I had met scientists from Cambridge, who talked like Rufusha,

'Where are you from originally?' I asked him.

'You're right, I do have an Oxbridge background,' he admitted, now able to read my thoughts. 'Well, was it Cambridge?' I continued.

'Yes, it was,' he said, adding, 'then I studied in the States, and went into commercial science work.'

'Was that in the 1950s?' I asked.

'Yes,' he said.

This was beginning to sound like an interrogation, but it wasn't meant to be. I was just trying to make sense of things.

'So, you must have been to other planets before Planet Atman?' I asked.

'I started off working on Mars, and my work took me outside the solar system,' said Rufusha. 'I dropped in on Adia's planet for a short time, but that was on the way to Atman.'

'Your name can't have been Rufusha originally, surely, if you're from the UK?' I said.

'No, it was "Watt", you know, like the measure of electricity,' Rufusha replied.

'Why did you change it?' I asked.

'I found myself with a group of different people, and Rufusha fitted in better.'

I tried to imagine what it must be like, going out in to space, working with many different people, and taking the decision to leave Earth for good. That would mean cutting off all connections to previous family, friends and roots. Rufusha read my thoughts.

'I could still go back to Earth, if I wished, but my life is here now, and I don't want to.' Based on what I had seen of Planet Atman, I didn't blame him.

That night, I realised that Adia had not been there when I passed on the Green upgrade to the others, and next morning I visited her invisibly, to see if it would be a convenient time to pass on the high frequency energy. S/he was sitting in front of a mirror, putting on eye makeup. Her partner, whose name was Amos, was standing in the hall. Without interrupting her, I transmitted the Green energy. Adia stood up and looked round.

Then s/he said to her partner, 'You know that phone call I got from work asking me to come in, because something special had happened? I think it just happened to me too. I feel so happy.'

S/he put her hand on Amos's arm, and he immediately received the same thing. 'So do I,' he said.

Just then, Sholouf arrived with an official car to collect Adia and take her to work, so I returned to Earth.

GEIA: ONE-GENDER PLANET

During the morning, I became dimly aware that Rufusha and his senior colleagues were looking in on me, and watching whenever US Mafia ghouls tried to attack me. The Atman scientists had learned how to tune into Earth, and were studying how we lived. Rufusha caught my eye.

'Have you got a moment?' he asked.

'Sure,' I said, and in an instant, I was back on planet Atman.

'We saw you being attacked. Is that part of the war on your planet?' It seemed simplest just to say yes.

'Earth is much more developed than our world is,' Rufusha continued. 'We need to make progress. How do you go about creating infrastructure projects using your abilities?'

'You can create them by your intention,' I said. 'What did you have in mind?' Rufusha went off to check with his colleagues.

When he came back, he said, 'It is possible for a new building to be created on the other side of the road over there.'

I looked across the road to where Rufusha was pointing. The ground was stony scrub land. 'Do you need to prepare the ground first?' I asked.

'No,' said Rufusha, 'it should be all right.'

'Do you know in detail what you want?' I asked.

'Yes,' said Rufusha.

'OK,' I said, 'I'm going to take whatever is in your mind and transfer it into material form.'

I willed the blueprint Rufusha had in his mind to take shape. Immediately, a large glass building appeared. It looked very modern compared to the other buildings on Planet Atman. Rufusha looked pleased, so it must have been what he wanted. While he went to admire his new creation, I turned to Arthurus, as I wanted to ask him about Adia's people.

Just recently, I took a trip to find Adia's home planet, which was fairly nearby. It was a tropical paradise, with warm breezes, exotic plants and trees, and attractive sandy bays. The surrounding hills were dotted with modest, oblong, one-storey houses, designed for single occupancy. The front of each house was made of glass, and looked like a conservatory. The back of each house was covered over and built into the hills behind.

The main shopping area consisted of run-down buildings, made from poor-quality grey concrete, and peeling, painted metal. It felt like a shanty town. Rightly or wrongly, I got the impression that Adia's race were regarded like second-class citizens.

'Are Adia's people all one gender?' I asked Arthurus.

'Yes, they are,' he said.

'How do they reproduce?' I asked, in what I hoped was a discreet manner.

'They do it by themselves,' replied Arthurus.

'Oh, you mean parthenogenesis,' I said.

'Just a minute,' said Rufusha, who had re-joined us, 'Can someone bring a dictionary?'

He looked up 'parthenogenesis' — which according to Wikipedia, is 'a natural form of asexual reproduction in which growth and development of embryos occurs without

43

fertilisation by sperm.' I heard Adia laughing loudly. She had just come in, and picked up what we were talking about.

'We give birth by ourselves,' she said, 'but we can have sex between our legs as well,' she added, smiling broadly.

'So, would you describe yourself as male or female?' I asked.

'I prefer to use the word "feminine",' said Adia, waving her arm in a graceful gesture.

'Fine,' I thought, 'that clarifies that!'

But the questions would keep coming.

'What sort of sewage infrastructure do you have on your planet?' I asked Rufusha.

'Oh, we don't need anything like that here,' he replied, 'Everything that we excrete is immediately disintegrated. It's the way it works on our planet.'

'Maybe you don't need to eat that much?' I asked, thinking that these people might be moving towards a less material existence.

'No, we don't need to,' said Rufusha.

'Then those sandwiches that I saw being served on plates in the evening...?' I continued. 'That would be a main meal for us,' said Rufusha.

'I noticed a self-service restaurant in your training institution,' I said. 'That seemed to offer quite a substantial meal.'

'Oh, that's all fruit,' said Rufusha. 'Our digestion is not affected much by eating fruit.'

'Would you like to be able to create whatever you want to eat or drink?' I asked.

Everyone was interested in that, so I made small tables, which I call magick restaurant tables. They provide whatever you want to eat or drink, if you look at the top of the table and think what you want. Rufusha wanted to make a table too. He produced one in beige wood, about two feet square with legs a foot high.

'Stop there,' said Adia, 'I want to get a drink.'

A takeaway cup appeared, filled with liquid. She drank some of it. 'Mm, delicious!' she said.

'Let me have a go,' said Sholouf, grabbing the cup. He took a sip.

'Ugh! That's horrible! Why do you like it?' he asked.

'It's what I'm used to,' said Adia.

I explained that the tables were designed to give each person the experience that they wanted from the food or drink, and that sharing with others probably wouldn't work, as everyone's tastes were different.

'How long do people live for on your planet?' asked Rufusha.

'Oh, a lot longer now,' I said, 'The average in developed countries is well over seventy years. What is the average on your planet?'

'Usually about sixty years,' said Rufusha, smiling wryly. 'Some of us are almost there now.'

I knew he was talking about himself and many of his friends, although I suspected that he must be older than that. But it was hard to tell, because people age differently outside Earth.

'Did you know, that with your new abilities, you can have a younger appearance and a younger physical age?' I asked. 'In fact, you can change your appearance in any way you like.'

'Excuse me a minute,' said Rufusha, and he left the room.

When he reappeared, he had changed a lot. Before, you

would guess he was in his late fifties. Now, he still looked senior, but his face was firm and his body was toned. He no longer stooped, and appeared physically fit and in good shape. His hair was more substantial, and darker, greying slightly at the temples.

'Wow!' I thought. 'These people are getting the idea quickly.'

Next day, the Parliamentary assembly debated whether to offer their new-found abilities to everyone on their planet. They were competing to stand up and speak in favour of doing this. Then the Speaker said, 'All those in favour, say "yes".'

Everyone stood up, shouting, 'YES!' So that was that.

That evening, I remembered Adia's home planet, and how beautiful, yet under-funded it was. I felt guilty that I had not gone there already to turn it Green. I tuned into its frequency, and immediately, I was back there, swimming in its warm tropical waters. I looked up at the luxuriant banks, and my eyes followed the footpaths that led up to a series of small houses built into the side of a ravine.

I could see two mauve-haired people trying to fix a crack in the Perspex door of their house. The door would not shut properly.

'Let every subatomic particle on this planet go Green,' I announced.

There was a moment's silence, and then I heard laughter, and shouts of happiness echoing round the bay.

'Well, I think we can fix this all right now,' said the person who had been struggling with the door. In a moment, the door was fixed, and the house had expanded in size, with an artistic creation that looked like a Perspex snail shell on the roof. In fact, it was an air-conditioning feature. I heard footsteps running down to the shore. The beautiful, mauve-haired inhabitants of the planet were diving into the sea, and floating there, talking to each other.

'At last! We don't have to go to work any more,' said one.

A parent leading a six-year-old child by the hand, joined the others in the sea. The child climbed onto the parent's back, as s/he swam around. All they wanted was to enjoy the beauty of their planet. A group of locals had gathered on the banks of the ravine, talking and laughing together. There was something I wanted to know, so I appeared in the water beside the swimming group.

'What is the name of your planet?' I asked.

One of the people sitting on the bank, whose name was Tera, shouted back, 'It's Geia, that's G-E-I-A.'

I recognised the name, which on Earth is spelt Gaia. It is the name of Mother Earth in ancient Greek literature. I could see why people from Earth might give the planet that name, as at first sight it seemed to be populated by women. In fact, a genderless, androgynous state was closer to the truth.

'Did the Americans give your planet that name?' I asked.

'Yes,' said Tera, 'The Americans gave it that name.'

'But the planet must have had a name before,' I thought to myself.

'It's OK, we can go with that for now,' Tera explained, reading my mind, 'We have our own language and our own name, but we only use that when we are alone.'

'Why did you go to work on other planets?' I asked.

'We struggled to survive on our planet' another Geian called Sahra replied. 'But haven't you always lived on this planet?'

I continued, 'If so, have you always struggled to survive?'

47

'Oh, no,' Tera explained. 'It was after the British came to our planet. We seemed to become less important than them, and our way of life suffered.'

'When was this?' I asked.

'In the 1920s,' said Tera.

'So, what happened to the British?' I asked.

'They left after a few years, but by then we had lost our traditional way of life,' said Sahra. That explained a lot! I knew that the British had to wind down their space programme after the First World War.

'But your main street has buildings from the 1960s,' I continued.

'Oh, that was the Americans,' said Sahra. 'They also came here once, and built the main street… but we had to ask them to leave.'

'Why was that?' I asked.

'They wanted us to work as their servants, and we wouldn't let that happen, not on our own planet,' said Sahra firmly.

I left the swimmers and looked back at the houses lining the side of the ravine. The two people who had been fixing their door were now in their living room, creating a salad meal of fruits and plants just by using their minds. I was glad to think that the inhabitants of this beautiful planet could now reclaim their independence, and no longer needed to rely on work on other planets for their survival.

INCREDIBILITY GAP

Back on Earth, I was working with the authorities in the United States, to catch as many Mafia and Islamic State terrorists as possible, before they could carry out laser, sonic and electromagnetic attacks on vulnerable people in North America and Europe.

The United States' military were proactive in tracing all the underground terrorist facilities in America, digging them up, and eradicating the so-called 'ghouls' — people operating within an electromagnetic persona for criminal purposes. (The best analogy for this technology occurs in the movie *Avatar*.) As a result, the covert terrorists moved their operations just south of the US border into Mexico. The Mexican authorities were cooperating with the United States' military, in order to resolve the problem.

As the number of electromagnetic criminals in North America reduced, terrorists were recruiting people from Mexico, Asia and Africa, promising them employment in the US as a reward for their services. These services included attacks on me, from underground bases in Mexico and the US, using electromagnetic force fields to create environments superimposed on my house in the British Isles. When that happened, I sent the terrorists, dead or alive, back to the location from which they entered the electromagnetic state.

That was a fairly sensitive operation, as no government

wants piles of ghouls suddenly appearing from underground hideouts. In terms of human existence, ghouls could be described as half dead and half undead. To avoid causing concern to local people, the Mexican government built large tents over areas where bodies appeared, so that specialist American and Mexican military personnel could dispose of the ghouls in private.

One morning, I woke to a concerted attack launched on my bedroom from Mexico, by several units of terrorists from the United States, guided by managers from the Irish Republic. As the ghouls aimed their weapons at me, I could hear them muttering, 'This is for you, putrid little pooer,' and 'Let's get rid of the blasted little bleater.'

After sending about forty of them back to Mexico, I got fed up and decapitated one of them, who was firing at me from outside my bedroom window. It caused the rest of the rabble to run away, but I heard a gasp from above my right shoulder. It was Rufusha. He and his friends had been watching the whole thing. As people on his planet are all very peaceful, it must have been a shock to witness the death.

'Hello Martha, yes we have been watching you,' Rufusha said. 'We have started to fill in the gaps in our understanding about Earth, and there are many things we need to know.'

'Oh, hello Rufusha,' I said, 'I was just dealing with an attack from US terrorists in the electromagnetic environment.'

'Yes, we saw it all,' Rufusha confirmed.

What I did not realise was that other people from a space station near Earth were also listening in on me. And when Rufusha started talking to me, the people on the space station got a 'crossed line' and were able to hear people from Planet Atman as well.

I heard a cry from the space station.

'Oh! There are people outside Earth talking to her, from somewhere else. That's not possible!' Then I saw a man in a space suit fall from the space station right into the US ghouls' border control portal.

'Oh dear, now what!' I thought.

I went straight down to the US ghouls' portal to see what had happened. Unusually, there was nobody on the gate, and the vertically operated doors were pulled down. Making myself invisible, I went through the closed doors. Inside, I could see several border guards standing round, while a doctor was examining a patient on a couch in a treatment room. The patient was a young man wearing a heavy-duty space suit.

I moved closer to try and find out what was going on. The young man, whose name was Natt, was in shock. He was crying and resisting the attempts of the treatment team to remove his space suit. What was going on? I tuned into the universal computer for an explanation.

It turned out that Natt had been on the outside of his space station, carrying out routine duties. His space suit's communication system had picked up the conversation between Rufusha and myself. Discovering that there were humans living normally on an unknown planet, talking to someone on Earth, had sent Natt into shock. He risked falling off the space station, and he needed medical help. So, his space station controller had made an emergency request for permission to transmit Natt down to the US military centre in New York. *4

Natt was still highly traumatised. You may think you could handle that, but hearing aliens talking in real life, even if they once came from Earth, is enough to unhinge anybody at first.

'It's not true! It can't be! If we are already on distant planets, why didn't they tell us? We've a right to know such things,' Natt sobbed.

To bring him out of shock, I sent Natt the total Green package. He stopped crying and let out a long sigh.

'I'm all right now. It's OK. Can I go please?'

'I'm afraid it's not as easy as that,' said the doctor. 'You didn't arrive in the normal way, and we can't just put you back without the proper procedures. And anyway, you need to be kept in overnight for observation.'

Suddenly, the treatment team brightened up and gave a cheer.

'Ah, here's the man who can sort all this. Thank goodness for that!'

An unassuming, senior-looking man in a white lab coat walked into the room. Although I had not seen him for over a year, I recognised him immediately. It was Elliot, the man I called the 'Chief Scientist' — see *Kiss Terror Goodbye*. Whatever was going on, he was always the one in charge and the one called to fix things. He worked with NATO as part of the US Military, and was the top boss of the US electromagnetic immigration portal that dealt with ghouls. I must have switched off my invisibility by mistake, as Elliot looked up at me and smiled.

'Hi Martha, come on in,' he said.

'I just did something to help calm Natt,' I said, feeling that an explanation was required for my intervention, particularly as Natt was now looking more cheerful.

'Can I go back now?' repeated Natt.

'Would you like me to send him back?' I asked.

'If you wouldn't mind,' said Elliot.

I surrounded Natt in an electromagnetic envelope and said, 'Return back where you came from.'

Then I followed him, to make sure everything was all right.

Natt landed inside a space station of the type that routinely orbits the Earth. He arrived on a reclining work chair in the control room, looking out into space from the viewing deck.

If you've seen the movie 'The Matrix,' you will recognise the reclining couches that the Matrix team used to keep their bodies secure while they went on electromagnetic missions. Natt's space station was light, bright and sunny, with white couches. There were soft carpets on the floor, and shiny modern fittings to hold the monitoring screens and other technical fixtures around the ceiling and viewing deck.

As Natt arrived back on his couch, uniformed technical operators in the room crowded round him. 'Are you all right, Natt?' one of them asked.

'I'm fine now,' he replied, heaving himself off the couch, still in his space suit. A group of children peeped round the door.

'Can we come in?' asked one of them.

They clustered round Natt anxiously. It seemed that in terms of life on the space station, all these people were family, and whatever happened to one family member affected everyone else. I did not want to intrude on things that were not my business, so I returned to the US immigration portal.

Elliot was surrounded by people in white lab coats, chatting and joking in a relaxed manner. When I returned, he said, 'What have you been up to, cruising around in space?'

'I was looking for dinosaur planets,' I replied.

I haven't mentioned my trips to dinosaur planets here, as this book would be twice as long if I did. 'Dinosaur planets!' laughed Elliot, 'I love dinosaur planets. Did you find any?'

'Oh yes!' I said excitedly. 'And I saw huge megalosaurs, a blue archaeopteryx, giant green flying lizards and white giraffes with black stripes like zebras.'

As it happened, Elliot shared my interest in dinosaurs, but I suspected I was taking up the great man's time.

'Well, I'd better be going,' I said, and left.

VIEW FROM THE SPACE STATION

Next morning, I looked back over the previous day's developments, and tried to make sense of what had happened. I remembered how shocked Natt was when he discovered that there were people from Earth already living on other planets.

But Elliott and the US border guards were not at all shocked, and had clearly known about people living on other planets for a long time. I worked with Elliott for over a year, and he never mentioned it.

I guessed that the information carried a very high military security classification, which prevented people from discussing these matters. But it could not go on forever, or it would create a two-tier society — an elite group who were 'in the know' and the vast majority of the world population, who did not know anything.

'But how many people in authority do know about Earth space exploration programmes?' I thought. There was no answer to this. I remembered what Natt had said:

'Why didn't they tell us?'

There seemed to be no answer to that either. 'I wonder how Natt is?' I thought.

In invisibility mode, I looked in on the operations room in the space station. It was dark now, and no one was there. I could just make out the reclining couches and viewing deck of the space station. A ten-year old boy slipped into the room and climbed onto one of the couches. He was playing at being an astronaut. A man came looking for him, and persuaded him it was time to go to bed.

After he left, I sat on the couch and looked out through the window of the viewing deck. Not too far away, I could see the Earth, partially in view. It was not quite as blue as pictures of Earth I had seen. There was quite a lot of cloud, but it was still a wonderful sight.

I decided to take a look at the station from the outside. It was hexagonal in shape. Extending above it was a docking station device that looked like a Ferris wheel. It was made up of straight lines connected by circular nodal points. Standing on the roof of the station, were two men in heavy-duty space suits with ladders, and one of them was Natt. The other was a man called Abe. I landed next to the men.

'Hi Natt, how are you?' I asked.

'I was just saying, I keep expecting you to appear, wasn't I, Abe?' said Natt.

'Yes, just this minute,' said Abe.

'It didn't seem that things could just finish without an explanation,' continued Natt.

'Well, I have a few questions too,' I said. 'How come you heard me talking to people on another planet from your space station?'

Natt smiled.

'You operate from an ultrasound system, and when we are outside working here, so do we.'

"Lots of people on Earth use ultrasound communications these days,' I said, thinking of all the Mafia and terrorist groups who use it. 'How do you filter out the interference?'

'Oh, we can fine-tune our reception,' said Natt. 'I couldn't

56

help hearing you talking to someone very interesting. But when I realised where he was broadcasting from, my mind just flipped.'

'How did you suddenly appear down on Earth?' I asked.

'Our station control operations team sent me down, because they were concerned about what had happened to me,' Natt explained.

'What are you both doing out here?' I asked.

'Cleaning the outside structure,' said Abe. 'You'd be amazed how much gumf gets stuck to it. The stuff is floating about everywhere. Some of it is sticky dust, and some of it is rubbish left by space ships.'

'So that's what the men in space suits were doing on the outside of the mothership in the other galaxy,' I thought. 'They were cleaning it up.'

Abe fixed a ladder against the lowest section of the Ferris wheel. He began climbing up it. Natt switched on a machine that looked like a leaf-blower, and started blowing dust off the roof of the space station.

'Look at that,' said Abe, pointing to a piece of paper that had got stuck in one of the higher spokes of the Ferris wheel. 'Ugh, it's disgusting!'

'Would you like me to remove it?' I asked.

'Yes please, that would save me the trouble,' Abe replied.

I mentally circled the paper in an electromagnetic field and put it in a clear plastic bag, which I created, before handing it to Natt. Then I selected the entire space station, both inside and out, together with the Ferris wheel, and said, 'Let everything be as clean and work as well as on the first day it was produced, every billionth of a second, forever!'

Suddenly, everything was shiny and new. Both men

gasped. 'Now that will save us a lot of trouble,' said Abe.

I turned to Natt.

'Has everybody on your space station received the package of Green energy that I gave you?' I asked. 'It can be passed on just by touching people on the arm.'

'Yes, thank you,' said Natt. 'Everyone on the space station has received the full package.'

'Would you like to be able to have the same abilities that I taught myself?' I asked.

'That would make life a lot easier,' said Natt.

So I selected them both in an electromagnetic field, and passed everything on to them. Now that the space station had been cleaned up, the two men went back inside and changed out of their suits. I noticed how much cleaner and fresher the space station was inside now.

Natt wanted a cigarette, which surprisingly, the rules allowed. He stood in an outer chamber, which did not communicate with the rest of the space station. His senior officer looked in on him, as if he wanted a word, but seeing him smoking, decided not to bother him.

In fact, after going Green, Natt found smoking did nothing for him, and he stubbed out his cigarette in less than a minute. But he still had an empty feeling inside. Abe joined Natt in the outer chamber, and we continued chatting. There was something I felt Natt ought to be aware of, and I thought he could handle it now.

'You know, Natt,' I said, 'when I visited a space station in another galaxy, I saw a group of men in space suits who could have been your brothers.'

Natt stared at me intently.

'Other people have said similar things to me,' he said.

'I've also seen a photo of astronauts who look just like me.'

'When I was in another galaxy,' I continued, 'a man told me that his parents came from the United States, and that thirty years ago, they went to a space station near Earth, where they produced children who grew in an artificial womb. After birth, the children were taken to the planet where they now live.'

A tear rolled down Natt's cheek.

'They could be my family,' he said. 'Will I ever get to meet them?'

'Well, there could be quite a few of them,' I said. 'You never know when or where you might meet up. But what if you did? Would it change things for you?'

'I don't know,' said Natt. 'I just don't know.'

'Well, keep an open mind,' I said. 'Don't forget, anything is possible.' There was another question I wanted to ask.

'There are several children on the space station,' I said. 'Where do they come from?'

'Oh, they come from different bases in the solar system. We call them "hybrids",' said Natt. 'That's because they are partly from out there and partly from Earth,' said Abe.

'So they are the product of two Earth parents, are they?' I continued.

'Yes,' said Abe.

'Well, they certainly looked like Earth kids to me,' I added, 'Why are they on this space station?'

'"It's so they can see the Earth, and get used to the idea of going back there,' Abe replied.

'How would that work?' I asked. 'If they've never been on Earth before, felt Earth gravity, or seen our houses, cars and cities, it's going to take time.'

'They start off in a secure military compound, and take it

from there, but I don't know much about the details of that,' said Abe.

I could see the senior officer coming in our direction.

'I guess I'd better go,' I said. 'I don't want to delay your work. Thank you for your time and for the information.'

The two men waved goodbye and I left. As I went, I could still hear them talking through the ultrasound system, even though they were out of sight. I heard Abe's voice. 'What else could I do? I had to say something.'

'I know, it's so difficult.' That was Natt's voice speaking now. 'At least she came back.'

I got the impression that there was more to the story of the children, that Abe and Natt were not allowed to discuss with me. But I did not understand the significance of that at the time.

FINDING NATT'S FAMILY

Next day, I kept thinking about Natt's unusual situation. Here was a young man who never knew his parents, had no family support, no cultural links, and had spent most of his life on space stations. He desperately wanted to get in touch with his roots and to find his own people, but he had little chance of doing so.

I felt sorry for him, and wanted to help. But if I did, it might seem that I was interfering in things that were none of my business. Also, I had to be careful not to do anything that would upset Natt's emotional state.

'Well, at least I could do research about Natt's people,' I thought.

Lots of men looked like Natt, but they weren't sufficiently similar to be the same family. But what would it mean to be from the same family, for someone like Natt?

It was likely that we were looking for a particular batch of humans that had been produced from the eggs and sperm of one man and one woman from Earth. Most likely, they would all be male, because the people behind the space programmes were looking to produce a space workforce. That much I could guess. But there could be many batches involving the sperm of one man, not necessarily using eggs from the same woman.

'Would it matter that much if the match was only half identical?' I thought.

Picturing Natt in my mind, I sent a request to the universal computer, to find the best match for Natt's ethnic group. Suddenly the environment changed. It was early evening, just after sunset. A small village of square grey huts with dark windows appeared. The huts were dotted around a bay, and there were wooden landing piers. The sea lapped quietly against the shore.

The huts had washing lines outside. I could see clothes pegs on the lines, but there seemed to be nothing attached to them. Further up the hill, a man in rough grey jeans, and an old, maroon, chunky-knit top came up the stone stairs from a basement. He walked down to a washing line on the shoreline, and began checking the clothes pegs. After a while, I worked out that something was attached to the pegs. It was there, but it was invisible. The man was feeling along the edge of whatever it was that the clothes pegs were holding.

'Oh, could it be a kind of fishing net?' I thought.

That would make sense. The whole place could easily be a small fishing village. At that moment, five men who looked like Natt came running up the steps from the basement area. They were laughing and joking amongst themselves. They went over to one of the huts. Outside, on a stone seat cut into the hill, an older man in an off-white, chunky-knit jumper and grey jeans, seemed to have fallen asleep.

Going to sleep on this planet could be pretty instantaneous. People had to look out for each other, in case they fell asleep before they got home. The men put their arms under the sleeping man's shoulders and lifted him up. They carried him down the basement steps and into a room with several wooden tables and chairs. There were a few men sitting at a table, and one was holding a glass filled with brown liquid.

At one end of the room there was an empty fireplace, with a wooden shelf over it. On the shelf there was a dusty painting of trees and hills, and a small, beige, ceramic jug. The scene looked exactly like a village pub.

Several men, all looking very much like Natt, emerged from the pub basement and moved towards a row of huts a little way back from the sea front. Each man had his own hut, which was well-lit and warm inside, behind the dark window blinds. Each hut contained a low bed, a small, wooden wardrobe, and low wooden shelves for the men's possessions. The men split up and went into their huts.

One of the men, whose name was Arturo, came out again, and began checking the transparent fishing net hanging out to dry outside his hut. He stood looking out to sea in the dusk.

'Will I ever find my own special friend?' he thought, his heart filling with sadness.

It seemed as if the universe was nudging me into action, but what could I do, without barging in and causing all sorts of trouble? How could I be sure that Natt was the friend that Arturo was looking for? Natt might not like this planet, or he might hate being a fisherman. Then I had an idea, which worked like an old-fashioned introduction agency. I would look in my mental archive for a photo of Natt on the roof of the space station, and leave it for Arturo to find.

I printed out the photo and taking care to keep myself invisible, dropped the picture in front of Arturo It came out quite large, the size of a poster. When the poster dropped down in front of Arturo, he gave a cry of surprise. 'Hey, where did that come from?'

He picked it up and looked at it. Two men, who heard Arturo's voice, came out of the hut next door. They could see him staring at the picture.

'What's that?' one of them asked.

'I don't know,' said Arturo. 'It just fell down in front of me.' He continued to stare at the picture.

'Let's have a look,' said the other man, peering over his shoulder. Then he gave a shout to his mates in the other huts.

'Hey, everyone, come and look at this! Look what Art has found.' Several men came running out.

'Who is that man?' asked one of them.

'Look! He's wearing the uniform of a space captain!' said another.

The men thronged round the picture. They took it into Arturo's hut, and nailed it on his wall. One of his friends put his arm on Arturo's shoulder.

'He's yours now,' he said.

Arturo just sat there, looking at the picture. 'So far, so good,' I thought.

I returned to the space station where Natt was working. It was night. I went to the outer smoking room and left a photo of Arturo there on the floor. My plan was that next time Natt went to have a cigarette, he would find it. But it was not to be. Natt's boss opened the door and looked in. Seeing the picture lying on the floor, he seized it in an irritated manner and tore it apart.

'I'm definitely not having anything like that here,' he muttered to himself, as he hurried down a corridor.

He chucked the torn photo in a plastic folder positioned in a holder along the wall, which must have been the space station equivalent of a waste bin. I felt sad that things hadn't worked out as intended, and I remade the photo. At that moment I heard footsteps scurrying along. A thin boy of about twelve, wearing dark, ragged clothes appeared. He quickly grabbed the photo, took a look at it, rolled it up and stuck it in his shirt. Then he raced off.

I followed the boy as he weaved his way through the network of corridors. He came to a door and opened it. I caught sight of the operations room with the viewing deck and the reclining couches. A man with headphones and a visor pushed to one side, was lying on the main couch. I moved closer. It was Natt, and he was fast asleep.

The young lad came in and pulling the rolled-up photo out of his shirt, placed it reverently on Natt's chest. Then quick as a shot, he disappeared. Almost immediately, Natt's boss looked into the room. Natt was lying there, sleeping like a child, and he obviously hadn't seen the photo yet.

Natt's boss saw what had happened, and took in the situation. He turned on his heel and left, closing the door quietly. Half an hour afterwards, Abe came in to take over from Natt. He touched his arm, and Natt woke up.

'What's this?' Natt mumbled sleepily.

He looked at the picture of Arturo, standing by his fishing net, staring out to sea. 'It's me, isn't it?' he thought. 'But it can't be. Who is it?'

He turned to Abe.

'How did this get here?' he asked, handing it to Abe. Abe looked at the photo.

'You said you wanted to find your family, didn't you? I reckon she's gone and done it, and now she's left this for you.'

Natt was looking at Arturo's picture more closely. 'I have to find him,' he said.

He went through all the possibilities of how he could do that, but he couldn't come up with a solution. Then he remembered what I had said about giving him the same abilities as I had got.

'I wonder…' he said.

A moment later, he was standing on the grass in the fishing village, holding the picture, and Arturo was standing there, looking back at him.

'You came back!' Arturo whispered.

'Yes,' said Natt, 'I've come back.'

The two men strolled by the sea shore, talking under the stars. Arturo showed Natt the fishing village where he lived. They walked hand in hand, talking about how they had each missed that special person that should have been there with them. Arturo sobbed on Natt's shoulder. He felt a weight lift off his heart.

The two men sat by the shore, watching the waves flowing on the sand. One of Arturo 's friends came out of the pub and joined them for a while. Then Natt fell asleep, leaning against Arturo. The two fishermen lifted Natt up and placed him on a bed in an empty hut nearby. This would be Natt's hut from now on.

Next day, I went back to see how the fishermen were getting on. The village was deserted. The men were further along below the cliffs, working in sandy bays. They waded into the shallow waters and set out their nets on the bottom of the sea. There were shoals of fish all along the coast line. At first, I thought they were eels, but on closer inspection, they turned out to be long, thin fish, with markings like mackerel.

The men returned at lunchtime, to check the nets. There were fish lying on the nets and swarming around above them. With expert movements, the men scooped up the nets, catching lots of fish in them, and dumping the fish and nets in wooden wheelbarrows. The men washed their nets and hung them up to dry on clothes lines. Then they killed the fish and hung them up on clothes lines as well, securing them with tiny hooks.

I spotted Arturo showing Natt what to do. There were lots of fishermen sitting round on stone walls now. Arturo reached up and took a fish from the clothes line. He removed the head and internal organs, and bit into the raw fish with obvious enjoyment. Then taking a knife, he cut off a good size chunk and offered it to Natt. Natt took a cautious first bite, but soon he was enjoying the fish as well.

'So, no problems there,' I thought, as I left.

When I got back to the space station, there was a group of four and five-year-old, mixed-race children standing round Natt's chair. They were waiting patiently for him to come back. I explained to them that Natt wasn't coming back. A small, dark-skinned girl with a mass of black curls said, 'I want to go where Natt is.' The others all said the same.

'I don't think that is going to be possible,' I said. 'Who is going to feed and clothe you, and provide beds for you? You can't expect Natt to do that. He has to learn how to look after himself first.'

'You don't know that. You haven't asked him,' said a tiny boy.

These kids had all been given the 'complete Green package' and they weren't going to be put off that easily.

'All right,' I said, 'I will go and ask him.'

So off I went. When I arrived in the fishing village, all the younger men were outside laughing and playing a game on the grass. On seeing me, Natt grabbed me and threw me up in the air. The others circled round, planning to catch me and do it again. It was their way of bonding, and they all did it to each other. But I wasn't having that at my age. I flew out of the circle, onto the ground, and made myself six feet high.

'Oh, what a pity,' said Natt. 'We were all going to catch you but you spoiled it.' He looked at me for a minute and added, 'I don't remember you being quite so tall, either.'

'I'm glad to see you have settled in so well,' I said, coming back to my normal height. 'There's something I've come to ask you. The children are missing you, and they want to come and live here with you. They asked me to find out from you if they could do that.'

'I don't think that would work here,' said Natt, 'but give me a moment to discuss it with the others.' He went down into the basement of the pub, where other young men were now gathering. Shortly afterwards, he emerged with three of his friends.

'No,' he said, firmly. 'Tell them they can't come.'

'Thanks. I'll let them know,' I said. 'By the way, has everybody here received "the full package"?'

'Yes,' said Natt, 'that's why they are all so full of energy. They are enjoying having perfect health.'

'"And have they had all the abilities that I transmitted to you?' I continued.

'Oh, no, I forgot,' said Natt.

'How would it be if I gave everybody on this planet the full package, and the same abilities that I have learned?' I asked.

Natt and his friends accepted my offer, so I turned the planet Green and passed my abilities on to everyone on their planet. They hadn't had a chance to find out what that really meant, so I did a small demonstration.

'Is there anything you need that you haven't got?' I asked.

By now, the whole fishing community was sitting outside on the grass or on rocks, holding glasses of beer. They considered my question.

'Now that we have perfect health, we've got just about all we want,' said one of them.

'How about new fishing nets?' said another. 'We could do with those, and you know how long it takes to make them.'

I materialised a small, wooden block that looked like a cell phone. 'Hold this and say you want more fishing nets,' I suggested.

The man tried it out and a pile of white, transparent nets appeared. 'Hey, that'll keep me going for a while,' he laughed.

'Now everyone, imagine you are holding one of the wooden blocks, and look in your hand and see if you have got one,' I said.

Everyone could do that.

'You don't need the wooden block to make things you want,' I explained. 'But it can be helpful just to get you started.'

The men began making wooden chairs and wooden storage units to go in their huts. 'Don't forget you can make clothes too,' I added. 'And have you tried one of these?'

I made a small, low table that would fit easily into a hut, and said, 'Let this table give you whatever you want to eat or drink, if you look at the top of it and think what you want.'

One of the men came forward and looked at the top of the table. A glass of beer appeared.

'Not very imaginative,' I thought, 'considering they've all just had a beer, but at least they've got the idea.'

Natt was lying on the grass, his head resting on one hand, a glass of beer in the other. He looked relaxed and free. I was glad things had worked out well for him.

'Well, I must be going now,' I said, and I waved goodbye. I had to get back to the children, before they started turning up on Natt's planet by themselves. When I got back to the space station, eleven children were standing waiting.

'Well,' said the little girl, 'what did Natt say?'

'He said no,' I replied, 'because he wants what's best for you, and he knows that staying with him isn't the best thing for you.'

This was a hard message for the children to receive. They looked downcast and I felt helpless, not knowing what would be best for them. I tuned into the universal computer.

'Let the children's fundamental needs be met in the best way possible,' I said. The children looked at me expectantly, but nothing happened.

'What has changed?' asked one child.

I had to admit that I didn't know. There was a silence. Then suddenly two huge gold and white figures flashed past the window outside the viewing deck. Another two flashed by as well. I raced outside to see what was going on. There were four tall angels standing on the roof of the space station. They had golden skin and golden wings, and they all wore long, white robes.

'One in each hand, that makes eight,' said an angel, in a matter-of-fact way. 'We need another two.'

Two more angels came rushing into view and landed on the space station. When in flight, they looked like otters do when swimming underwater, with their wings and clothes all streaming backward in the astral wind. Next moment, they were inside the operations room, and each one was holding two children by the hand. My mind jumped to the small boy in rags that I had seen earlier in the space station corridor.

'Can he go too?' I asked.

'No,' said an angel, 'only these ones,' and they rose up into the air and flew off through the glass of the viewing deck, clutching a child in each hand.

As if on cue, the small, ragged boy appeared, standing hesitantly beside me. I suddenly noticed that he wasn't a physical human. He was slightly transparent. But he looked exactly like an ordinary child. His face fell when he realised that he had been left behind. He stepped closer to me, seeking reassurance as I was the only person left.

At that moment, a long, golden arm reached into the room, picked the boy up by the waist, and pulled him out of the space station. The angels' maths had been correct. There were twelve children, so they needed six angels to take one child in each hand.

I became aware of someone looking into the room. It was Natt's boss. 'All the children have gone,' I said.

'Yes, I know,' he replied. 'And Natt has gone too. I don't know why I'm still here.' He looked around despairingly.

'Is there somewhere else you would rather be?' I asked. 'Of course,' he said.

I guessed that Natt and Abe had not got round to passing on all their abilities, though everyone on the space station had the full package of 'cleverest brain and perfect health.' I offered Natt's boss all my abilities, and he immediately accepted them. He removed his official badge, and disappeared. I don't know where he went, but it had to be somewhere better than the space station.

'I suppose I'd better go and find Abe now,' I thought, 'to let him know that Natt's boss and all the children have gone.'

Tuning into Abe's frequency, I found myself in a different part of the space station, in the staff common room. Eight men including Abe, all in the same khaki workwear, were sitting round a table, laughing and talking. Abe looked up when I appeared.

'Sorry to interrupt your work break,' I said, 'but I ought to let you know that your boss has gone.' The men let out a cheer.

'Thanks for telling us,' they said. 'Now we can relax.'

"All the children have gone as well,' I said.

'Did they go with our boss?' asked one of the men.

'No,' I said, 'angels took them.'

When I said the word 'angels,' all the men put their faces on the table, pretending to be afraid. 'We mustn't see angels. We mustn't talk about angels,' they chorused.

'It's forbidden for us to discuss them,' explained Abe. 'But in fact, we see them flying by quite often.' He got up and went out.

'I'd better let headquarters know there have been a few personnel changes,' he said over his shoulder, as he went down the corridor.

The rest of the men looked bewildered by what had happened. 'Did Abe pass on all his abilities to you?' I asked.

'No,' said the men, 'but if he's got something extra, we want it too.'

So I passed everything on to them. At first, they didn't believe in it. Then one of them flew up to the ceiling. The other men burst out laughing. Another man joined him. I left them all trying out their new 'wings.' Really, there was no need to pass on these abilities, as everyone who went Green was capable of developing them, but it shortened the learning curve.

I went out into the darkness of space. The artificial light inside the space station tired my eyes, but the permanent darkness of space made me long for natural light. I knew that if you go up to higher frequencies, it is light all the time, but my own frequency did not permit me to do that.

Using thought, I created an inflatable bed and lay on it. Four angels appeared. This time they were wearing dark green robes. Each one held a golden lyre with four strings. They began playing the lyres while singing at the same time. I strained my ears to hear the music and the voices, as they were very faint, though beautiful. The voices were wordless, what on Earth we would call 'voice as instrument.' In other words, they were just going 'Aaah.' *5

After a while, the angels took hold of my bed and tugged it upwards. We reached a place where dawn seemed to be breaking. My heart thrilled as the dark clouds gave way to clear sky. This was as far up as I was likely to get.

ADVANCED SCOUT SHIPS

Next morning, I heard a talk on the radio about space travel, given by a scientist from California. The scientist said that future space travel would not involve actual movement, simply an alteration of the spaceship's positioning locator. Apparently, everything in the universe has, as part of its inherent properties, a frequency which indicates its location. If an object moves, its frequency locator alters. So, to move a vehicle in space, all that is necessary is to adjust the frequency of the vehicle's location to that of the place you want to go to, and by default, the vehicle is in the new location.

I mentioned this technology to Rufusha on one of my visits to Planet Atman. Rufusha was surprised that I knew about it, because it is classified as secret on his planet. But after I raised the subject, he confirmed that they used it.

I was able to tune into the mind of the Californian giving the radio talk, and get a picture of the spacecraft he was referring to. It was round, like a flying saucer, about thirty to forty feet in diameter. We would call it a scout ship. The interior was unfurnished, but there was a light brown shelf around the inner wall, with fitted orange cushions for people to sit on. A wide window like a viewing deck ran all the way round the ship, from the top of the seating up to the ceiling. The speaker explained that the ship was piloted by a brain-computer interface. Exactly how this operated was not explained, but it meant that the pilot could drive the ship just by thought.

It occurred to me that scientists on Planet Atman might be interested in this technology, as they were keen to update their technologies. So I connected with Rufusha's frequency, and went to see if it was convenient to talk to him. Rufusha was sitting at his desk. By now, I had worked out that he was a very senior figure from the scientific community on his planet, so I was cautious about interrupting him.

Rufusha looked up as I appeared.

'Oh, hi,' he said, 'Did you want to discuss something?'

'Well, if it's not inconvenient,' I said, 'I just learnt about a new development in space transport, and thought you might be interested in seeing examples of it.'

'Where does the technology come from?' Rufusha asked.

I mentioned the Californian scientist who had given the talk on the radio. Rufusha brightened up immediately.

'Oh well, if that's where it comes from, I'm sure our scientists would be most interested,' he said. 'Just give me a minute, and I'll see if I can contact them.'

Rufusha arranged everything, and soon we were in what looked like a large aircraft hangar, where aerodynamic research was carried out. Several white-coated scientists were standing listening, as Rufusha outlined my proposal.

'If I produce one of the space craft, would you be able to "back-engineer" it?' I asked. The scientists looked at each other.

'We would certainly like to try,' said one of them. The others nodded.

'Where would you like me to put the ship?' I asked.

'Over there,' said one of the scientists, pointing to a space next to the hangar wall.

Visualising what had been in the mind of the Californian scientist, I recreated the space vehicle. Now, I know nothing about space craft myself, or how to open the doors on one. But luckily the scientists had no problem with that. As far as the technology went, they were halfway there already. Rufusha was the first into the space craft.

'How does it operate?' he asked.

'It uses a brain-computer interface with radio wave communications,' I said.

'That happens to be my specialism,' said Rufusha, 'Can I have a go?'

As I understand it, all that is required is for the pilot to interact with the computer that drives the space craft, using thought. If you're used to that and you can activate it, the rest is straightforward. Rufusha connected with the spacecraft and the lights came on.

'Let's go for a short trip,' he said.

We went to a pleasant rural town, and landed in a field. Having proved that it could be done, we returned to the aircraft hangar. I made a second spacecraft, to give the scientists more material to work on. They were interested in everything, including the lightweight materials used to make the craft. While the scientists were investigating the properties of the space vehicles, Rufusha turned to me.

'I think you ought to know,' he said, 'since your last visit to the fishermen, Natt has been disappointed that you haven't gone to live there. Having never had any family, Natt has now found where he belongs. He seems to expect that you will become a kind of grandmother figure on his planet.'

'Oh dear,' I thought, 'Now what have I got myself into,

and how am I going to get myself out of it?'

Clearly, Natt needed a motherly person to be there in the background, to provide emotional support and reassurance. I could not do it myself, but perhaps someone else could. I tuned into the universal computer, and asked it to find the best person.

An image of a spry, elderly woman came into my mind. She wore a long, black robe and hood just like my black puffa coat, and her grey hair was tied in a graceful knot at the back of her head. When I appeared in front of her, she was sitting on a boulder in a field. She didn't seem particularly surprised at my arrival.

'Hello,' I said.

I paused. I just couldn't think how to ask this lady to drop everything, go to live on a different planet, and take care of a group of fishermen!

'I know why you're here,' said the lady, whose name was Cara.

'Thank goodness,' I said. 'I can't quite find the right words. It seems such a lot to ask.'

'You will have to give me all your abilities and relevant background memories, if I am to take your place,' said Cara.

'Fine,' I replied, and using my intention, gave her the 'full package' — all my abilities and knowledge of everything relating to Natt.

Cara stood up.

'I am ready for this,' she said. 'Don't worry, I have much more patience than you. I will be able to provide what is required, just by sitting there. Let's go.'

Next thing, we were standing in the fishing village. Natt came running over immediately. 'Who is this you have brought?' he asked.

'Natt, this is Cara,' I said. 'I am sorry I can't stay with you permanently, but Cara can. She already knows all about you.'

Natt stepped back. His voice trembled.

'What do you mean?' he said. 'When I saw you arrive I thought you had come back for good. But you are saying you can't do that.'

Cara stood up and went over to Natt. She put her hand on his arm. 'I am going to be here permanently,' she said.

When Cara touched Natt's arm, he relaxed, and looked into her face. 'Really? You will be here permanently, always?'

'Yes,' said Cara. 'Now, I will need somewhere to live. Have you got a place for me?'

'We already have a place prepared,' said Natt, and he led her over to a brand-new hut that the men had built for me.

It was bigger than the other huts, and had been created using thought. Natt opened the door of the hut and Cara looked inside.

'Very nice,' she said.

Using her abilities, she added all the interior decoration and extra furnishings that she wanted. After that, she found a large boulder, like the one she had been resting on before, and sat on it. The men came up in twos and threes to talk to her.

'Can you tell us about your life before you came here?' one of them asked.

'Well, it all began a long time ago, before you were here...' said Cara.

At that point, I decided to fade out of the picture, as it seemed a good moment to go. But next day, I checked up on the fishing village, just to make sure things were going all right. Cara was sitting on the boulder, talking to Natt.

'Do you think we should expand our village?' asked Natt. 'There are friends living a short way from here. We could invite them to join us.'

'I can't advise you on that,' said Cara. 'What do the rest of the men feel about it? Have you discussed it with them?'

Arturo came over.

'We are always going over the hill to join them when they go out fishing,' he said, 'but we want them to come over here.'

'Have you asked them yet?' Cara smiled encouragingly. 'Oh yes, we've asked them.'

Two more men joined in.

'And what did they say?' asked Cara.

'They like the idea.' One of the older fishermen, whose name was Hegero, added his voice to the discussion.

'You don't need my advice on this,' laughed Cara.

'I know,' said Hegero, 'But we like having someone to talk things over with us.'

By now, the men were sitting in a semi-circle round Cara. Everything seemed to be going well. I wanted to say thank you to Cara for what she was doing. She was the ideal person to become a village elder. So I created a few rose petals and showered them on her, to celebrate her new role.

'What are these?' asked Hegero, 'I've never seen anything like this before.'

'Nor have I,' said Cara.

'They are flower petals,' I said, joining the group.

'What are flowers?' asked Arturo, picking up one of the petals.

I realised there were no flowers on their planet. In fact, most of the planets I visited, didn't have flowers, perhaps because they didn't have any insects. I created a fragrant

79

peach-coloured rose in an ornamental planter, and presented it to Cara. All the men came running to see the new creation.

'I suppose they'll want it to last forever,' I thought, so I made it into a living sculpture.

Then I did another one. This time I made a blue daisy plant. Each blue flower had a golden centre. The men looked at it in astonishment. They took it into their basement drinking room, and put it on the shelf over the fireplace.

Now that Cara had taken over, it was time for me to go.

'Thank you, Cara. Goodbye and good luck!' I called, as I left.

'My pleasure,' Cara called back.

PLANET OF THE RUFFIANS

When I met Abe and Natt on the roof of the space station, they told me that the children I saw there were being returned to a military base on Earth, after living on other planets. But something about their story didn't add up. I wanted to find out more. It was to be a while before I discovered the truth.

I leaped out into the darkness of space, looking for clues about children and kept on going. A large, grey, gas giant loomed up in front of me. I ploughed straight through it, and out the other side. Strange yellow scout ships, flashed in front of my eyes. A small, dark planet appeared and I went straight into it, and landed with a bump. It was not a gas planet and the ground felt much like that on Earth.

As I sat there rubbing my bruised nose, shadowy troll-like figures came and sat round me. Then more figures joined in. Soon they were pressing in on all sides. One of them leaned in on me. 'I could eat you!' it said.

'Why, are you hungry?' I replied.

'None of us have eaten for a long time,' said the troll. 'Right,' I thought, 'I'd better deal with this.'

Selecting the entire planet, I said, 'Let everyone on the planet have the 'full Green package,' and let them all have mini tables which give them the food and drink they want, whenever they select from the table.'

After getting the cleverest brains in the universe and

perfect health, the trolls stopped looking troll-like. I explained how to use the tables and they got on with eating right away. But to my horror, the food they wanted to eat was half-opened packets of biscuits, canned fizzy drinks and leftovers from cast-off takeaway meals. I guess that's what they were used to eating, when food came their way. After eating, they threw the packaging all over the ground.

'Let all waste, human and non-human, disintegrate as soon as it touches the ground,' I announced, as there was a problem with both, and piles of poo were noticeably dotted about.

'And let all the men have fresh clothes of their choice,' I added.

I sat on the ground and watched as the men stretched out on their backs, fast asleep. When people are in an electromagnetic form, as these men were, they do not need to eat as frequently as in their normal state. But it was obvious that the men hadn't eaten for a long time. Luckily, whatever they chose to eat would be good for them, provided it came from the 'magick' tables.

As I stared into the darkness, more yellow lights flashed by. I could now see that they were small, yellow spacecraft shaped like boots. They had a hollow vertical part that joined onto a flat support below, with a curved front section where the toe of a boot would be.

The darkness began to fade, and turning round, I saw a dark planet behind us, that was blocking the sun. As the sun moved round the dark planet, day began to dawn. The ground, now cleaned and tidied up, was covered with middle-aged men, who, despite their fresh clothes, were in a pretty rough state. As the sun rose, they began to wake up and help themselves to more food.

'Where do you come from?' I asked.

'We come from the United States,' said one of them, whose name was Rob.

'How many of you are there,' I continued.

'About two hundred thousand of us,' said Rob.

'Where are the rest?' I asked.

Looking round, the place seemed relatively deserted. 'Oh, they're scattered about all over the planet,' said Rob.

'What are you doing here?' I asked.

'We got sent here, because we didn't do what we were asked to,' came the explanation.

'I've heard that one before,' I thought to myself.

The US Mafia's low-level ghouls were always saying that. What they meant was that they got sent here because they were caught red-handed doing illegal activities, and didn't stop doing them when they were ordered to. The men finished their second meal and began preparing to lie down again. So I created self-cleaning, dark-brown easy chairs with foot rests for them.

'This is the life,' said Rob, stretching out on a chair. He turned to his mate, a man called Tom.

'It's a pity there aren't any plants left,' he said. 'It used to look really nice when there were things growing round the water here.'

He pointed to a small stream running through the bare earth. 'What happened to the plants?' I asked.

'We ate them,' said Tom.

'Let all the plants on the planet come back to life,' I said.

Immediately, the dark earth was covered with grass, bushes, shrubs and clusters of trees.

'That's better,' said Rob.

Some of the men got up and began pulling leaves off the bushes and eating them. 'Stop that!' shouted Tom. 'You don't need to eat them any more. Eat from the tables.'

"But we like the leaves,' replied one of the men.

'Then make more leaves using the tables, idiot,' said Rob. 'Honestly, some people are hopeless.'

The men started using the magick tables to make a salad of leaves. I decided it would be helpful to give them all the same abilities I had got.

'I'd really like to see oaks over there,' said Rob, 'but I don't suppose I'll be allowed to.'

He made them anyway. There they stood, huge and overpowering, blocking the sunlight. 'You can't do that!' shouted a man wearing a flat hat, whose name was Con.

'Get rid of the horrible things,' shouted another man.

Rob sighed. 'Oh, all right,' he said, and replaced them with silver birch trees.

'Much better, thank you,' said Con.

'Well at least that was settled amicably,' I thought, preparing to leave.

No sooner had I turned my back than the men started taking off their new trousers and tops, and running around in their shirts and trunks.

'Why are you doing that?' I asked.

'We're saving our best clothes for later,' Con replied.

'You don't need to do that,' I said. 'Don't forget your new abilities. Now you can have best clothes every day.'

After a little encouragement, the men put their clothes on again. 'Con, where is the planet you came from?' I asked.

'It is in that direction,' said Con, pointing away from the

sun.

Con pointed in completely the wrong direction, but as it turned out, it didn't matter. I set off to find the planet, and stopped at the first one I met. I was surprised to see a 'ghouls' net' all round the outside. I have seen these nets on Earth, built by the US military, Russia and Pakistan, amongst others, to keep out electromagnetic terrorists. Of course, keeping them out is one thing, but if you have home-grown ones on the inside, that is a different matter.

In order to get through the ghouls' net, I had to disaggregate my body into sub-atomic particles and reassemble it on the other side. Then I arrived in a lush tropical world, filled with trees and plants, which was called Planet Zardur. The sun shone on the shining, blue sea, and large, black birds nestled in a canopy of luxuriant glossy, green leaves.

I pushed through a jungle 'til I came to a clearing, where a black, hexagonal building stood amidst the trees. The walls were smooth and polished, like black granite, and the roof rose to a central point. A tall, Caucasian man, wearing a white short-sleeved shirt, and trousers, came out through a revolving glass door. Inside, the reception area was a pleasant, well-lit facade with beige interior decoration, a registration desk, and on one side, a spiral staircase which descended to several underground levels.

I went down the staircase into a beige, carpeted corridor. The interior of the building was like an opera house, with layers of corridors in a semi-circle. I went into the rooms leading from the corridors. In each one it was the same. Twenty-five men in white shirts and trousers were sitting at beige tables, while white-coated lecturers demonstrated mathematics and algebraic theorems on white boards. I was in Planet Zardur's College of Mathematics.

Three semi-circles down, in the centre at the back, there was a refreshment area. Ten middle-aged tutors were sitting round a dark wooden table, laughing and talking. A wooden plaque on the wall behind them displayed their names in gold letters.

'Can you pass the fish up from the end please?' asked one of them.

While the fish was being passed up the table, a messenger arrived. He carried an envelope on a tray and handed it to the vice-principal at the head of the table.

'How strange,' said the vice principal, as he opened it. 'What does it say?' asked the man sitting next to him.

'It's from upstairs. Got to go immediately, excuse me everyone,' came the reply.

The vice-principal hurried up the stairs to the principal's large, wood-panelled office.

'Do come in Hiram,' said the principal. 'Sorry to interrupt your meal, but there's something I think you ought to know as soon as possible.'

'What's happened?' asked Hiram.

'I've just been notified by our security people that an intruder has been identified nearby.'

"An intruder?' echoed Hiram.

'Yes,' said the principal. 'Here's an image captured by the security cameras.'

He switched on a screen fixed to the wall above him. A picture of me in my long, black coat and hood appeared. It was an out-of-date image which I had stored in my mental archive. When people are in electromagnetic form, they either take on a prepared image, typically from a laptop computer, or they go with whatever self-image was last uppermost in their minds.

'I really must fix my image,' I thought.

Luckily, I had made myself invisible on entering the building, but if that was what I looked like, it was time for a makeover!

'Be on your guard, Hiram,' the principal continued, 'and if you see anything, let me know.'

While he was speaking, I mentally changed into a long white coat. That was a mistake, as making the change removed my invisibility, just for a second.

'Oh, what was that!' cried the principal. 'Hiram, did you see it.'

"Yes,' cried Hiram, 'I saw it as well.'

'Right,' that's enough,' said the principal, getting to his feet, 'I'm going to see the head of security now.'

'I'd better go,' I thought, and I switched myself back to the dark planet of the ruffians. Rob, Tom and Con were still sitting there.

'You know,' said Rob, picking up the conversation as if I had never left, 'if there's one thing I miss, it's a good smoke.'

'You can make what you need by yourself now,' I reminded him.

Rob lit a pipe and began smoking it, but after two seconds he shook the contents out onto the ground.

'That was great,' he said, 'but somehow, I've had enough already.'

'Strange, that's not like you to give up so soon,' said Con.

'It's because when you create from thought, any cravings are removed,' I explained. I changed the subject.

'Have you ever thought about going home?' I asked.

'We can't go back now,' said Rob, 'we're not wanted.'

"How sad,' I thought.

Flipping a switch in my mind, I went straight back to Earth, to the US immigration authority's ghouls' portal.

'Hi,' I said, 'how are you placed to take in a large group of American ghouls from space?' The US official was not at all phased by this unusual request.

'How many are there?' he asked. 'About two hundred thousand,' I said.

The man shook his head, and turning towards the inside of the portal, he shouted: 'We can't take in two hundred thousand, can we?'

'No, we can't,' a man's voice shouted back. 'We can't even handle twenty thousand. It's quite impossible.'

I half-expected the US authorities to say that. On one occasion I brought in over thirty thousand, when I caused several units of ghouls to lose their electromagnetic buildings. The authorities had to open two baseball stadiums to accommodate them.

I went back to the planet of the ruffians, and settled down under the trees, where the men were sitting. At that moment, one of those yellow space craft, that looked like a large boot, landed. Two men got out. They were about five-foot high, with brown skin, collar-length, straight, dark hair, large, black eyes, and light, khaki uniforms. They headed straight for me.

'Who put the plants back on the planet?' asked the ship's captain.

'I did,' I said.

'Don't you know it's a breach of intergalactic law to interfere with indigenous life forms and their development?' he said, in an accusing tone of voice.

'These men are not an indigenous life form,' I said. 'They are from my planet. They stripped this planet because they had nothing to eat. Now that's been resolved, and I have put the plant life back as it was before.'

'What planet are you from?' asked the captain.

'Planet Earth,' I replied.

'Ah,' said the captain, 'in that case, the leaders of my planet would be interested to meet you. Would you be willing to accompany me on my ship?'

'Of course,' I said.

We went aboard the yellow ship. The tall part of the 'boot' was really a turret, positioned over the ship's engine. The ship was designed to hold up to six people inside the turret, with two on each level. It sped off into the darkness, leaving behind the ruffians' planet, now bathed in sunlight.

A brightly-lit planet came into view. It had rich, green, tropical plant life all over the land. High volcanic mountains provided a dramatic back drop. An orange stone city with municipal buildings built on stepped plateaus, like Mayan architecture, came into view. There were numerous walkways covered with bold, terracotta, ethnic textiles, which provided protection from the blazing sun. It was so colourful that it could have been mistaken for a Disneyland theme park.

We landed on a square airstrip, and climbed a series of up-hill walk-ways to an area where a large, wooden throne was standing. In front of the throne was a brown, polished stone about three feet square, with a gold, metal plaque in the middle of it.

The walkways teemed with people wearing yellow, spotted garments like leopard's skin, with brown cloaks thrown over one shoulder. The whole city was full of people, coming and going everywhere. Something about the way they looked reminded me of characters from Disney cartoons. A person who moved with the authority of a leader came up to the throne, and sat down on the ground next to it.

'We are called the In-Eu*6,' he announced. 'I am the head of this planet,' he added. I doubted that, as he did not sit on the throne, but I said nothing.

'This is our sacred stone,' the leader continued, pointing to the polished brown stone in front of him. 'We brought it with us when we came here. It is from our home planet.'

The leader lowered his voice confidentially.

'We have a favour to ask you,' he continued. 'You are from Earth?'

"Yes,' I said.

As I watched, a young man who seemed to be about fifteen years old, came and sat on the other side of the sacred stone. He wore a white robe and had a mop of long, curly, mouse-coloured hair.

Suddenly I read the leader's mind. The young man had been made to appear like a human from Earth — or their idea of what an Earthling would look like. They wanted me to take him back to Earth, and 'release him into the wild,' so that he could get through the Earth's military security defences, and let the rest of them in. I jumped up in shock.

'Oh no you don't!' I shouted.

All the people round me scattered, and as if a technician had flicked a switch, the whole scene faded, and I was left in space.

'It's not a planet at all,' I thought. 'The entire structure is a kind of mothership.' As I went back to the planet of the ruffians, a thought occurred to me.

'What if the people in the yellow space ships have bad intentions towards the ruffians' planet, now that it has plants and is habitable again? Maybe that's why they landed there in the first place.'

When I arrived back, most of the men had disappeared, but I could see Tom halfway up one of the silver birch trees, with Rob standing at the bottom.

'Can you see anything yet?' asked Rob.

'No,' said Tom.

'Climb up higher then,' said Rob.

'What are you doing,' I asked.

'We're trying to see what the other people are up to,' explained Tom, from his high perch. 'Trouble is, they've all gone off somewhere, and we don't even know which direction to walk in to find them.'

I looked down the hill and across a huge, flat plane that stretched to the horizon, with rocky hills on either side. I couldn't see anybody either.

'They can't have gone far,' I thought.

I took myself down to a rock that jutted out over the plain. As I thought, nine of the men were sitting in the shade underneath it. Climbing a tree wouldn't have helped to locate them from above.

'Here they are!' I shouted up to Tom.

Rob and Tom soon came down and joined the rest of their group. As they sat with their backs against the rock, admiring the panoramic view, I thought to myself:

'These men wouldn't stand a chance against any invaders. Whoever put them here should protect them. I must find out why they are here, and who put them here. In the meantime, I'd better build a protective screen around the planet that will keep invaders out.'

So I created a strong force-field around the planet. That would stop anyone from getting in, as long as they didn't have advanced technology that could get round what I had created. Then I set off for the planet with the mathematical university on it, to see if I could get answers to my questions.

PLANET OF BOILING MUD

Taking care to make myself properly invisible this time, I headed for Planet Zardur and the office of the college principal. He was sitting at his desk, and the vice-principal and five professors were standing round him.

'I'm told she is on her way here now,' said the principal.

'How irritating,' I thought. 'Someone's tipped them off.'

I did not like being second-guessed by these academics. But it was hardly surprising, given their high level of security. There were armed guards standing with weapons at the ready at the back of the room. That did not look encouraging. So I prepared an A3 sized poster with a picture of my image, and under it I wrote:

I AM FROM EARTH. I COME IN PEACE, TO ASK QUESTIONS ABOUT PEOPLE LIVING ON NEARBY PLANETS.

I dropped the paper on the desk, in front of the principal. 'Ah, good,' said the principal.

He nodded at the armed guards, who stepped back and stood at ease. Then I made myself visible. 'Oh, hello,' said the principal, 'Would you like to sit down?'

He pointed to a chair opposite him, and I sat down. 'Might I ask your name, please?' continued the principal.

'It's Martha,' I said.

'Would that be Martha Twine?' the principal enquired.

'Yes, how did you know?' I replied.

The principal picked up my first book. 'We have your book,' he said.

'Elliot is to blame for this,' I thought, referring to the US Military head of all things electromagnetic. 'Well, I've written another book since,' I said.

'Oh?' said the principal. 'We haven't got it.'

I created several copies of *Kiss Terror Goodbye* with pages that lit up like a tablet whenever you looked at them. The professors all took a copy. Now that the civilities were over, it was time to get down to business.

'So, how can I assist you?' asked the principal.

'There is a planet near you, with ruffians on it,' I said.

'Oh, those robbers,' said the principal. 'Yes, I know of it.'

'The men come from Earth, from the United States.' I said. 'They have stopped being criminals now, and their planet is back to normal. Do you know who brought them there, and where the people who brought them come from?'

'There is a planet I know of,' said the principal. 'People there may be responsible.'

"Can I have a picture of the planet?" I asked.

The principal obligingly reached for a file on his desk, and brought out a photograph of stars in space, with one particular planet in close up.

'Thank you, that is all I need on that,' I said, mentally archiving the photograph of the planet. 'There is something else,' I continued. 'There is another planet nearby, with a lot of small space craft flying around it.'

'Oh, you mean the yellow fellows,' said the principal.

'Yes, that's right,' I said. 'I think they intend to invade the planet of the ruffians. Also, they tried to get me to take one of them back to Earth, to get round our intergalactic security arrangements.'

'They don't pose a threat to us,' said the principal, 'as we have the same intergalactic security system as Earth, which I think you will agree, is the best available.'

'Undoubtedly,' I said.

'As far as the threat of Earth infiltration is concerned,' the principal added. 'I think you would be best to discuss that with Elliot. He seems to be the right man to deal with all that.'

The principal was right of course. Having got what I wanted, I felt it would be courteous to offer something in return, but perhaps these high-powered intellectuals did not need any mental enhancements.

'I don't suppose, in view of your advanced academic level, you would be interested in the package of enhancements that I generally offer to people?' I asked.

'Oh, I think we would be,' said the principal.

The professors brightened up visibly, as if they had already been briefed on all this. I thought I had better include all those poor students who had to study hours of algebra every day, so I said, 'Let everybody in this academic institution have the cleverest brain in the universe, perfect health of mind and body, and be able to pass it on to others by touching them on the arm.'

'Would you like me to pass on my other abilities as well?' I asked.

'You mean, flying through the air and appearing,' said the principal.

'Yes,' I said. 'All that sort of thing.'

The professors looked at each other. They were rightly concerned as to how far these additional abilities should be distributed.

'Perhaps we should restrict that to those of us that are in the room,' said the vice-principal.

At that moment, one of the students opened the door and looked in, unaware that a meeting was going on. In a gesture of inclusiveness, the principal beckoned him to come in.

'I think we can allow one more,' he said.

Then I transferred all my abilities to everyone in the room.

'How is that done?' asked the principal.

'It operates through a mind-computer interface with the universal computer,' I said.

'Do you think I could have the equations which demonstrate that?' said the principal.

I hesitated for a moment. Tuning into the universal computer, I announced, 'Create the equations requested in a booklet of A3 size.'

A booklet of A3 size appeared. The pages unfolded like a map. If you opened it up, it would form a single sheet of paper that just about covered the carpet. I handed it to the principal.

'Before I leave,' I said, 'would you like a table that gives you what you want to eat or drink if you look at the top of the table when making your selection?'

All the professors expressed an interest, so I specified the creation of a table that would blend in with the principal's decor. It had very long, wooden legs, and a small oblong top.

'Can I have one?' asked one of the professors.

'You can all make your own,' I said. 'Look at the original, and think "Make another".'

Immediately, all the academics had made their own table. They each created a fine crystal goblet, containing a sparkling wine. As I waved goodbye, they raised their glasses in a farewell toast.

'Cheers,' I called back as I left.

'Next stop will be the mysterious planet whose picture I just archived,' I thought.

But something made me check in on the planet of the ruffians first. It was true that I had put a forcefield round it for protection, but what if something went wrong? I decided to turn the planet Green at subatomic level. That way, even if the In-Eu landed, they wouldn't do any harm.

It was night as I arrived. On all sides, I could see yellow space ships attempting to enter the planet's atmosphere. None of them got through, which was a relief! I watched for an hour, as they tried repeatedly to get in from all angles, without success.

I went back next day to see what was going on. It was daylight, and on the vast plane below the rocks, lots of men were sitting together on stones that they had moved into circles. The stone circles gave the landscape a Neolithic look, but they were just for social purposes. Up above the clouds, there were yellow scout ships. They were located outside the planet's security forcefield, but were clearly visible.

Rob, Tom and Con were standing in one of the stone circles looking up at the alien space ships. 'Oh dear! Oh dear! Do you think we are safe?' said Rob

'I'm afraid they're going to attack,' Tom replied. I landed next to the men.

'Don't worry, they can't get in,' I said. 'They haven't got anywhere to live, that's why they are here.'

"They can't live here. We live here.' Con sounded anxious, despite my reassurance.

'No, they can't live here,' I said, in what I hoped was a

confident tone, 'In fact, I'm just on my way to find a place where they can live.'

'Better do it now, Martha.'

The urgency in Rob's voice convinced me that I better had do it now. I hurried off into the darkness of space, and tuned into the universal computer:

'Let me find a planet exactly right for the In-Eu,' I said.

I found myself hurtling through the universe without a clue where I was going. A dull, grey planet came into view. As I landed, I could tell that the temperature was quite warm and humid. The sky was cloudy and I noticed that the dry, rocky ground had almost nothing growing in it.

'Maybe it's just this part that's like that,' I thought. 'I'll move about until I find more welcoming terrain.' I crossed a ridge and looked down into a scooped-out valley. Then I got a shock. The entire valley

was moving. It was a lake of bubbling, brown mud. Mud had built up at the sides of the lake, like

walls.

'Looks like it would be good for building houses, when it cools down,' I thought.

I did a quick check over the entire area, to make sure there were no signs of other people living there. I moved down through rough, grassy slopes. There were plants, but nothing like the lush greenery I had seen on the In-Eu's mothership.

'I'd better make it more like what they're used to,' I thought.

So I created Mayan-style architecture, a few walk-ways and tropical shrubs. I still had my doubts about the place, but the universe never gets things wrong, so I decided to go with what I'd got. Tuning into the In-Eu's sacred stone, I found their mothership, and landed in their throne room. The head man strode up to me. His face looked hostile.

'Why are you here again?' he said.

It was more of a challenge than a question.

'I've found a place for you to live,' I said. 'It seems to be uninhabited, but I don't know if it's what you would like.'

'Take us there, and we will decide,' he said.

Selecting the entire mothership, I visualised the new planet, and parked the mothership in an orbit around it. The In-Eu looked across at the rocks and brown mud.

'Looks fine to me,' said their leader. 'Just like home. We'll try it.'

I created stabilisers to fix the mothership in a docking position, and put bridges from the mothership onto the rocky ground. The In-Eu poured off the ship in their thousands. Others landed in scout ships. Using their own mental abilities, they transported everything off the mothership, and set about designing their new home. Then they discovered the bubbling mud lake.

'Wonderful! We are back home!' they shouted.

I made a mental note never to doubt the reliability of the universal computer. The In-Eu started dismantling the Mayan architecture I had made for them.

'Don't you want that?' I asked.

'Oh no,' said one of them, who seemed to be overseeing the building projects. 'We just made our ship look like that, so that people from Earth could relate to us.'

'So you won't want the bushes,' I said.

'What? Oh, you mean the pot plants,' the man said. 'We'll leave the pot plants,' he said.

'How do you know what people on Earth would be used to? Have you been there?' I asked.

'We've never been to Earth,' he replied, 'but we've been close to several planets where people from Earth are living, and we've been able to receive your television transmissions.'

'So that explains the Disneyland theme parks,' I thought.

The idea of people on other planets watching Disney cartoon films was bizarre. As I watched, two people respectfully carried the In-Eu's sacred stone off the mothership and placed it in a new location. They had already started using the cool mud from the side of the mud lake to create dwellings. The houses looked like those of ancient people at Montezuma's Castle in Arizona, and blended perfectly with the environment.

'Why did you have to leave your previous planet?' I asked.

In response to my question, several In-Eu people came running up to me. They handed me what looked like a large, round cassette tape.

'How are you supposed to read this?' I thought.

In the end, I decided to let my mind absorb it. As I watched, a dark, volcanic planet, with rocky terrain appeared. There was a huge crack in the ground, and glowing red magma began spurting out of it high into the sky, like fireworks, covering the planet in all directions. Shadowy people in drab clothes were racing out of the area, carrying all their possessions onto a dark spherical mothership. The planet did not break up, but the surface became uninhabitable.

I turned to a group of young people who were watching me.

'I have seen your story,' I said, 'but I don't recognise you. The people I saw all wore dark clothing. They don't look anything like you.'

'Oh, we only started looking like this when we wanted to

contact Earth people,' said one of them. 'We copied what Earth people were wearing on television.'

'Ah,' I said, 'so what do you normally wear?'

The group of young In-Eu suddenly transformed themselves in front of my eyes, and disappeared. I couldn't see them anywhere.

'We look like this,' came a voice from what looked like a nearby boulder.

The boulder stood up and waved its arms. It was just a dark, loose, sack-like cloth bag, with three holes for the head and arms. If the In-Eu withdrew their arms and heads inside the cloth, they looked like stones.

'Why do you wear those dark clothes?' I asked.

The young people clustered round me, anxious that I should understand and appreciate their way of life.

'It is to blend with the ground,' said one of them. 'We come from the rocks, and we feel part of the rocks. So it is natural for us to dress like this.'

A group of senior elders came towards me, wearing dark brown robes. They looked like the real leaders of the In-Eu. The person describing himself as their leader earlier had just been a spokesperson. I turned to look in their direction. The hills were now covered with dark brown walls and mud-coloured dwellings with flat roofs. The buildings looked as if they had grown out of the rocks surrounding them.

One of the senior elders stepped forward.

'Thank you for leading us to our new planet,' he said. 'We were sure that Earth people would be the ones to help us find it, and events have proved that we were right to follow our intuition.'

'I am glad that this place is acceptable,' I replied. I said goodbye to the In-Eu and left.

BAD BOSTON PLANET

Now that the In-Eu had left the area, I headed for the planet suggested by the principal of the Mathematics University as being able to advise about the ruffians. The planet was covered with grey clouds. I dived in, and landed in thick woods. In front of me, I could see a long line of men in flat caps and woollen overcoats, carrying what looked like Ruger semi-automatic rifles. The men behaved like servants, marching slowly through the woods in an unending line. They seemed to be patrolling the area.

Making myself invisible, I made my way out of the woods, which lined the tops of the hills, down into the green slopes of the valley below. I could see a small town, with a mix of stone, brick and wooden houses. In the middle of the town was a fine municipal building in a light-coloured brick. It had two floors, with long arched windows on the second floor, very like Faneuil Hall, which was originally built in the 19th century, in Boston, Massachusetts, but without the bell tower. The interior decor was brown wood, with brown wooden benches, and a wood-panelled first-floor gallery.

Outside the building, a black, vintage Rolls Royce pulled up. It was a New Phantom, also known as a Phantom I, built in Springfield Massachusetts between 1925 and 1929. Two men in flat caps and overcoats got out and went into the building, where an official debate was in progress. They were shown up to the first-floor gallery. I guessed that the two men, who seemed to be servants, had been nominated to act as token members of the public.

Inside the building, a Parliamentary session was taking place. The Speaker, whose name was Lord Deveral, and who sounded British, wore a heavy white wig and long black robe. About twenty men were taking part in a debate. As the two men sat down in the gallery, one of the debaters said to the man next to him.

'I see our two stalwarts have arrived.'

'Quite so, quite so,' said Lord Deveral. 'Shall we continue?' The debate carried on.

'We must move with the times. Our clients expect it,' said one man.

'But how are we to fund the necessary works to modernise?' asked a man sitting on the other side of the hall.

'It's not for us to decide. Surely, we should seek advice from our higher authorities?' another man asserted.

'I don't agree, at all,' said a fourth man, 'We should be operating as an autonomous unit.'

At that moment, a tall, imposing woman in a long, dark-turquoise taffeta dress and small hat, swept into the hall. She marched up to Lord Deveral and said, 'Hubert, why are you still talking? You are already late for lunch.'

'Oh, very good, dear,' said Lord Deveral. 'I propose that we adjourn immediately.'

All the men left the building and got into a line of New Phantom cars. They made their way out of town and up the wide, tarmac road to a hill, where another building, similar to the Parliamentary building, but with columns at the front, stood surrounded by green fields.

The Parliamentary group were ushered into a large hall with a long table. Lady Deveral sat at the head of the table, and her husband took the seat at the other end. The Members of Parliament filled the chairs in between. They all stood up to say grace before the meal. The lady of the house spoke first:

'I believe in God, the Father Almighty.'

'That's a rather short grace,' I thought.

It was as if she was repeating a half-remembered phrase from long ago. Each person round the table said the same short phrase, one after another. Then they all sat down, and women servants wearing dark brown dresses, cream hats and aprons, served food. Men servants in dark brown suits served drinks.

Another Phantom arrived, and the 'two stalwarts' got out. They were led down to the mezzanine floor, where they joined a group of servants sitting on benches round a wooden table. A butler asked if they would like whisky with their meal, which they gratefully accepted. Before they had finished eating, the servant girls were called to help upstairs.

They stood up hurriedly, mumbling, 'May the Lord make us truly thankful,' and pushed back the bench they were sitting on, before rushing off to their work.

'Where do these people live?' I thought.

I rose above the town, and looking down, spotted small, dark, grey, brick terraced houses built in rows. They looked very like 1920s British housing, designed for poor people. Looking through the windows, I could see women in servants' uniforms, cleaning their houses and washing clothes by hand. There were no modern labour-saving devices. I had to remind myself that all this was happening in 2019.

On the other side of town was a tarmac air strip, leading to a building with a long reception area. A dark grey scout ship landed on the tarmac. Inside the ship, twenty men in their fifties, dressed like men from the planet of the ruffians, were sitting in rows. Their tables were covered with plastic cups, empty biscuit packets and soft drink cans. The men were in good spirits as they made their way out of the ship, escorted by a tall blonde air hostess in a smart modern uniform.

The men went into the reception area, where their mood changed. They stood respectfully in line to register for work. Their shoulders slouched, their clothes looked drab and ill fitting, and when they removed their hats, the few remaining wisps of hair on their heads floated untidily in all directions. It looked as if what they found on arrival was different from what they were expecting.

The air hostess cleared all the rubbish out of the scout ship and brought it into the reception area in a large plastic bin. She returned to the scout ship and waited for the pilot to prepare for take-off.

It began to get dark. I decided to go back to the woodlands and see if the patrol guards were still working there. On the way, I passed a large, fenced compound. Inside there were men crouched on the ground or lying down. The temperature had dropped, and they huddled together for warmth. They had been left outside without food, as a punishment for poor work.

When I got back to the woodlands, the patrol was still marching round the hills, as if on the lookout for trouble. It was soon clear why. Near where I was standing, a group of twenty men armed with guns and sticks was crawling along the ground. They selected victims to target from the night patrol, and grabbed their feet, pulled them to the ground. They gagged them and tied their hand behind their backs, before rolling them down the hill into the undergrowth.

One of the victims kicked off his shoes, displaying gnarled misshapen toes, as if to show that he would not try to resist or run away.

'Better not kill him,' said one of the attackers, 'or we could hang for it.'

The robbers took the guns and personal possessions of their victims and withdrew. They made their way towards the shops and commercial buildings in the valley below, intending to break in, and take what they could get.

Suddenly, a troop of tall, fit men dressed in black combat gear, armed with modern guns, surrounded the bandits and arrested them. The robbers were handcuffed and led away to the tarmac area, where a scout ship belonging to the security guards was waiting. As it took off, I joined the ship, invisibly. The robbers started talking to the security guards.

'We were promised homes and wages,' said one of them, whose name was Alf. 'But when we got here, we were put in hostels and given food, but no money.'

'The hours we worked were too long. At our time of life, it was impossible to do what was expected,' said another man, called Ray.

'We were kept like slaves, with the threat of no food if we didn't do our work right,' Alf continued. A third robber, whose name was Tim, told what had happened to him.

'I didn't produce enough wooden planks in the time allowed. So I was put out in the punishment yard, day and night, with no food, and only a bucket of water. Of course, I tried to escape, wouldn't you? I took food from the back of a shop, and went to live in the woodlands with the rest of the men.'

The head security guard, whose name was Slim, listened

sympathetically.

'I know,' he said, 'it's not right to treat people that way, but that's over now. We all have our jobs to do.'

He shrugged his shoulders. 'Will we die now?' asked Ray.

'No, I don't think you will,' said Slim. His voice had an air of mystery...

'In fact, where you're going, you could just be the lucky ones.'

"Where are we going?' asked Alf.

'Nearly there now,' replied Slim.

The scout ship came in to land on the planet of the ruffians. Rob, Tom and Con were sleeping nearby. The noise woke them. As they looked up, twenty men in their fifties, in drab clothes, emerged through the door of the scout ship. As soon as their feet touched the ground, they got 'the full package' — the cleverest brain in the universe and perfect health of mind and body. Slim and the other security guards jumped out too. Then they all got the Green energy.

'Yes!' shouted Slim, 'I knew it was true!'

He went back into the scout ship and touched the pilot on the arm. Immediately, the pilot got the full package. I guessed that this probably wasn't the first scout ship to land since the planet went Green, so word must have got around amongst the security guards.

Slim and his team got back into the scout ship and returned to the 'Boston' planet. On the way, I joined them, and introduced myself. Slim wanted to talk to me, but we all had things to do on the Boston planet, so we agreed to meet up on their mother ship, when our work was completed. When the scout ship landed on the Boston planet, Slim strode into the reception area, where a group of clerks were working late, finalising paperwork for the day's arrivals and departures, and announced, 'Let everyone on the planet have the same gifts and abilities as we have got.'

There were gasps around the room as everyone went Green. Men got up from their desks. A moment ago, they had been exhausted from long hours of work. Now they were refreshed, and their minds were opened. They would never be slaves again. They broke into quiet conversation as they put on their coats and went home to their wives in the servants' housing.

I followed them home. The women had already noticed that there had been a sudden change. One woman called Adeline, who I had seen earlier scrubbing the floor and washing linen, was sitting with her feet up, talking to a friend.

'I knew it! I just knew it was true, and now it's happened!' she said joyfully.

'How did you know?' asked her friend, Maddy.

Adeline reached into the pocket of her apron, and pulled out a battered wad of papers. 'It's written here in the notes. You know, the notes they send round to us.'

I looked at the type-written paper. It was an extract from *Kiss Terror Goodbye*, which had been smuggled into the planet by the security guards, and passed round secretly among the oppressed people.

'I know what I'm going to do now,' said Adeline, and she vanished.

I quickly followed her. Dawn was rising, and Adeline was sitting in a field on a hill, which overlooked a road below. Maddy appeared next to her.

'Found you!' said Maddy.

'You can't get away from me that easily.' Adeline laughed.

'This is the perfect place for my house,' she said. A large, pleasant house with its own drive and garden appeared.

'Mine is over there,' said Maddy, as another house suddenly materialised further up the hill. At that moment, the women's husbands, Will and Bernard, came into view, strolling together.

'Thought you'd be here,' said Will, giving Adeline a kiss. 'It's what you always dreamed of, your house in the country.'

'Let's go in,' said Adeline. Bernard looked at Maddy.

'Shall we?' he said, taking Maddy's hand. The two couples went into their new homes.

'It won't be long before the countryside is covered with houses,' I thought, 'but there's plenty of room for everyone.'

I went to see what was happening in Lord and Lady Deveral's palatial mansion. There were no servants downstairs. Lady Deveral was woken by her maid.

'Good morning, My Lady,' said the maid, but she did not curtsy. 'I think I ought to tell you that I won't be working for you after this. In fact, I am leaving now.'

The maid walked out and closed the door. Lord Deveral had woken up by now. Both he and his wife had been affected by the Green energy just like everyone else. They began to feel rather uncomfortable about their current position, and past behaviour.

'I think we had better make our own breakfast,' said Lord Deveral.

The couple dressed in modest, every-day clothes and went down to the kitchen. Lady Deveral cooked bacon and eggs, while Lord Deveral made toast. Just as they finished eating, the front door bell rang loudly several times. Lord Deveral answered it. A man in working clothes, holding a pitchfork, was standing outside.

'Lord Deveral,' he said, 'I've come to tell you your time is up. You are no longer in charge and you must leave this building now.'

'Oh, all right,' said Lord Deveral. 'I quite understand. We will leave. Just give us time to get our coats.'

He had no alternative. All his staff had left, and he had no way of enforcing his authority. He and Lady Deveral left the building on foot. They had no idea where they would go, or how they would live, but after the way they had treated people on their planet for years, they feared the worst.

When they arrived in the town centre, they were met by a crowd of people and put in one of the punishment compounds. They stayed there all day, and all they had was a bucket of water, just like the men they had imprisoned in the past. As evening came, they were each given a crust of bread. Since getting the Green energy, they now realised what monsters they had been before. Lady Deveral started crying.

'Here you are, Dear,' said her husband, trying to comfort her, and he gave her his crust.

At that point, the men in charge of them decided that Lord Deveral should be allowed to come out of the punishment compound, since he had proved he was a human being after all. He went off to help other older men who were working on new plans for roads to expand access to the countryside.

Lady Deveral was left on her own. She had to experience the indignity of peeing into a bucket in public, just like other prisoners. But no one was particularly interested. There was so much going on around the town. Modern buildings with labour-saving devices began to appear everywhere. The townspeople took care to ensure that the character of the town was not lost, and that buildings were placed in good order and according to architectural principles.

In the end, the women took pity on Lady Deveral and let her out.

'It's not right that she should be treated like that,' they said. 'Only men got put in the punishment compounds.'

'I am so very sorry for everything I did,' said Lady Deveral, tears pouring down her face. 'Something must have gone wrong with my brain. I can't bear to think about it.'

She was allowed to join a group of older women who were designing a new school complex, as a prototype to be used in future. She and her husband gave up their titles and became known as Hubert and Helen.

I went back to the planet of the ruffians to see what was going on. When I arrived, Rob, Tom and Con were sitting on a rock near where the scout ship had landed. A set of smart houses now filled the area. Tim, Alf, Ray and the other new arrivals were standing outside the houses.

'Are you sure you don't mind?' Ray asked.

'Oh no, that's fine,' said Rob. 'We can go down the hill a bit where our friends are.'

I made myself visible. The new arrivals saw me, and seemed to know who I was. 'Is this the woman you were talking about?' Tim asked Con.

'Yes, that's her,' Con replied.

'Hi, guys,' I said, 'I have good news for you! Your planet's been changed. The people are free. They have what they need and don't have to work for others any more.'

The new arrivals took in what I had said.

'In that case,' said Alf, 'I want to go back there,' and he sent himself straight back immediately. The others decided to return as well.

'Is it all right if we put things back like they were before?' asked Rob.

'Oh sure, do what you like. Must go now,' Ray replied, and he and the other arrivals wished themselves back home again.

Rob made the houses disappear. 'That's better,' said Tom.

'Much better,' said Con.

The three men went back to sleep

As previously agreed, I went to meet up with Slim and the other security guards. They were out in space, sitting on the outside of their mothership, without spacesuits or breathing apparatus.

'Hi,' said Slim. 'We thought you'd never come. We've been waiting for ages.'

'Sorry about that,' I replied. 'By the way, how come you can breathe unaided outside the mothership?'

'It only looks as if we're on the outside,' Slim explained. 'Well, we are outside, of course, but the ship's magnetic field extends for quite a way. The ship is designed to provide the same environment throughout its magnetic field.'

There was something I wanted to ask Slim. 'You're from America, aren't you?' I said.

'Yes,' said Slim, 'that's where we come from.'

'The older men you brought in your scout ships, how and where did you get hold of them?'

'You see,' said Slim, 'we used to work for the US space programme, in the military, so we had contacts. Our contacts came from the private sector. They were people who once worked with the US on the space programme.'

'All of us are ex-US military,' added Joe. 'Slim's second

in command. We lost our jobs, but we knew how to run our own show, and our private sector clients provided the ships and the equipment. Our business is transporting people and providing security services.'

'But the older men, where did they come from?' I persisted.

'Our clients had to let their older workers go,' said Slim. 'And they had a deal with the bigwigs on what you call the Boston planet, to bring in free labour. We got paid to bring the men in from Earth, and the Boston lot paid us to remove dissidents and put them where they wouldn't cause trouble. We picked that other planet, the one you call the planet of the ruffians, because it was nearby.'

'So your clients are the US Mafia?' I said.

'Indirectly, yes,' said Slim. 'We dealt directly with private sector scientists who used to work on the US space programme. They arranged for their business partners to send us their older workers, because they could not be let go on Earth. The workers knew too much and it was in everybody's interests for them to go off planet.'

'OK, I get it now,' I said.

'Well, if there's nothing else you want to know,' said Marty, another of Slim's crew, 'can we go?'

"Go where?' I asked.

'That's where we need your help,' said Marty, 'We understand that we have all the abilities, but we're not sure how to get what we want yet.'

'What is it that you want?' I asked.

'We want to quit and start a new life,' said Slim. 'But where can we go, and how can we find the way?'

I looked round to all the men sitting on the mothership.

'Well, anything is possible, what do you have in mind?' I asked.

'We want our own planet,' said Slim. 'Nothing too fancy, but quite like Earth. Once we've got our own place, we can bring our families and start again. It won't be like the old days, now that we have all the gifts and abilities. We think it can be better than Earth, with no war, no illness and no ageing.'

'You seem to have grasped what's possible very well,' I said. 'I think I can find you a place to start, but it might be safer if we went inside the ship, if we are going to do serious travelling.'

We all went inside, and I tuned into the universal computer, while the men watched.

'Let this ship find its way to the right planet that meets all the men's needs and expectations, now,' I said.

No sooner had the ship left than it arrived. We looked out of the windows of the viewing deck. In front of us was a large planet with grey and white clouds covering the entire surface.

'Doesn't look much fun to me,' I thought. 'I much prefer blue sky and sunshine.'

"What do you think?' I asked Slim, 'Do you want to take the ship in?'

All the men were looking excitedly at the planet. They didn't seem to be put off by the clouds at all. 'Yes, let's go,' said Marty.

'Joe, would you like to drive?' said Slim.

Joe took the controls and steered the ship towards the clouds. As we approached, the windows became covered with water droplets. At least they looked like water droplets, but it must have been 'designer water,' because as we went in, it started to get lighter, not darker. Light streamed in from all directions. I looked back into the darkness of space.

The stars seemed bigger and closer now. We were going through a kind of condensation belt at the top of the planet's atmosphere. The belt operated like one-way glass, with additional magnification caused by the planet's spherical shape, which created a lens effect. From the outside, it looked cloudy, and no one could see in. But from the inside, it was a sunny day, with a nearby star providing light and warmth. At night, the stars looked huge, thanks to the magnification effect.

Joe coasted down looking for a place to land. He floated over lakes and mountains towards a dry, grassy plain, and that's where the mothership landed. The ship was quite long, so it needed a large space, with firm ground underfoot.

The men checked the planetary atmosphere to assess if they would be able to breathe safely outside. The mix of nitrogen, oxygen and carbon dioxide gases was fairly similar to that of Earth. Marty put on breathing apparatus, and stepped outside. Slowly he removed his helmet, testing the air. His companions were ready to rescue him if anything went wrong, but nothing did. Soon, all the men were out there, big grins on their faces. The risk of danger was over, and they had arrived.

Slim wasted no time in announcing that everyone who set foot on the planet would have all the gifts and abilities that they had brought with them. Next thing, the men wished for their partners and children to join them! The place was full of people, laughing and hugging.

'We'd better make ourselves houses,' said Slim. 'What's the best way, Martha?'

'Ask your partners what they want,' I said. 'Take what's in their minds and materialise it, giving yourself plenty of space around each house.'

Soon, all kind of buildings began to appear.

'It doesn't matter if you want to change your mind, that is easily done,' I added. Then I faded out of the picture.

'You can always call me if you need help,' I whispered to Slim as I left.

'Thanks, Martha,' said Slim. 'I think we'll be all right.'

GREENING THE UNIVERSE

Next day, I needed a break. I plunged into the darkness of space, deciding not to plan in advance. 'I wonder what would happen if I tried to turn different parts of the universe Green,' I thought.

'Let everything in the universe go Green,' I announced.

The darkness got lighter, and I could just make out enormous oblong shapes leaping upwards, like great, grey whales. Still, there did not seem to have been much of an improvement. I tried again. 'Let every sub-atomic particle in the universe go Green.'

Everything went completely black for a moment, and there was a definite change. The space all round had changed colour. It was more of a mid-grey, and I could see the outlines of a landscape.

'Right,' I thought, 'Let's try that formula at higher frequency levels.'

At last, space was no longer always black. At higher frequency levels it was like early dawn. You could still see all the stars shining, but the background was a light grey. What a relief! I got so tired of it being dark all the time.

'Now let's go for the high jump,' I thought.

With all my strength, I aimed for the highest level I could possibly reach. It was like climbing a sheer mountain face. I felt I was clinging on by my fingers. At last, I got as far up as

I could. I rested for a minute and prepared to make things go Green, but as I looked round, I got a shock. There was the most enormous space building, right at this high level.

If you could imagine a city of long, metal pipes, linked by huge, spherical nodes, with nose cones at the end of each pipe, and all the pipes linked to each other by other metal pipes lying crosswise, that's what it looked like. It had the air of a strange baroque cathedral of gleaming, metal spires, lying on its side. But it was on such a grand scale that I couldn't estimate the length and width of each metal pipe. It could have been miles.

We were fairly close to the top of the frequency band within which human experience can operate in the universe. I could tell this, because not only was space less dark, but you could see the beginnings of light dawning up above the spaceship city. Also, there were angels flying about horizontally, all over the place.

In my view, angels are not impersonal do-gooders. From what I have observed, they are a high-frequency life form that live in the upper universe and above it. They have different personalities, and they do not automatically know the answers to every question that has ever been asked. By nature, they are teachers and guardians. They are friendly to all other life forms, and want to help reduce suffering. But like the military, they have their terms of engagement.

Anyway, to get back to the spaceship city, I had a hunch that the US military were involved, because the nose cones looked like US aircraft about the time of the Second World War. I try not to get in the way of the Earth's military, as, like everyone else, they have a job to do. But as I was about to send Green energy to everything, I thought I'd better check what was going on. Giving myself invisibility, I went into the spaceship city.

The city must have been several miles long and several miles wide. It was designed for long tours of duty, where people couldn't go back to Earth for over a year. To make up for this, the city had leisure areas which reproduced natural scenes on Earth. One was a large bay, with turquoise water lapping against golden sand, and an artificial sun shining down. Another was a huge prairie area with red poppies, and a stream running through it. I could hear bird song, though I couldn't see any birds.

Eventually, I found myself in a large amphitheatre, with seating for several hundred people. About half the seats were taken. On stage, senior people in military uniform were sitting in a semi-circle. One of them was dressed like a US general. The uniform did not match any current US military uniforms, but it was similar to those used during the Second World War. The general was making an announcement. 'Brace yourself men, it's coming any minute,' he ordered.

I guessed that he had received advance warning about my presence and my intentions, probably from Elliott.

'Well, I'd better get on with it,' I thought. Focusing my thoughts, I announced, 'Let every subatomic particle in the universe now go Green!'

There was the inverse of a flash, as everything went black. Then the frequency band of the universe that we were in rebooted itself with a brand-new upgrade.

'I hope everybody is all right,' I thought.

I checked up on the military amphitheatre. Men were just re-taking their seats, as if a minor earthquake had passed.

'Everything all right Charlie?' the general shouted.

'Yes, Sir,' came the reply from offstage.

119

'Well, perhaps we can get on then,' continued the general.

I didn't feel it was right to hang around, as they were obviously busy. But there were many things I wanted to ask. So I appeared in front of the general.

'Excuse me, Sir, may I ask you a question?' I said.

'Of course.' said the general, smiling.

'Do you have diversity in your workforce?' I asked. The general looked me straight in the eye.

'No, Ma'am,' he said, 'I'm sorry about that, but there it is.'

'What about family life?' I continued. 'Is there anything like that here?'

'Of course.' said the general. 'Look, let me introduce you to one of my aides, who will be happy to show you around.'

A fit-looking woman in uniform, in her thirties, stepped forward. 'Nice to meet you, please come with me,' she said.

'What is your name?' I asked.

The woman looked worried, and I guessed that her name might be classified information that she wasn't allowed to reveal.

'Oh, it doesn't matter,' I said.

'No, it's fine,' the woman said. 'You can call me "Red". That's what my friends call me.'

'OK, Red, let's go,' I said.

We climbed up a metal ladder that led to another level within the city, and at the top, a pair of automatic doors opened. Inside there was a long, carpeted area, filled with children aged four to six years old, all happily playing with toys on the floor. They looked exactly like children on Earth.

'How long is the tour of duty?' I asked, wondering if that was classified as well.

'Eighteen months,' said Red.

'And do the children just come back down to Earth at the end of it?'

'That's exactly what they do,' said Red.

We had reached the end of the long, carpeted room. Red touched a panel in the wall, and we switched mode to another area inside the city. It was a beautiful bay, with cliffs looking down on a beach.

'Oh, that's great!' I cried. 'Do you get to swim in it?'

'I'm just about to,' said Red, taking off her shoes.

Next minute, she had jumped from the cliff, and landed in the sea. I jumped after her, quickly changing into a wet suit. I looked up at the cliffs above, and there was the general, with several men. Without a second thought, the general dived in and swam with us. The other men did too. They were all doing the crawl. I was swimming by will, which did not involve using my arms and legs, and must have looked strange.

'When did you first come here?' I asked the general, 'Was it after the Second World War?'

The general laughed. 'I know I'm wearing this ancient uniform, but I'm not quite as old as that. We first came here in the 1960s.'

Even if the general arrived in the sixties, he was remarkably well preserved. I suspected that the high frequency location of the space city had something to do with it. Reading my mind, the general said, 'Yes, you're right. Nobody ages here.'

'Are you a peace-keeping force?' I asked.

'No,' said the general, 'That would suggest that there was a war going on, when there isn't. We are pursuing our role of making sure that the US military in space have everything they need in order to carry out their duties.'

After talking and swimming for a while, we reached the end of the bay. There was an arch in the rock, like a door, leading to a beautiful, sandy beach. I could have gone through the arch, but I felt I ought not to take up too much of the military's time. So I thanked the general and Red for their kind hospitality, and waving goodbye to everyone, I left the city.

Back outside in space, I noticed that the tops of the space city architecture now breached the boundary between the realm of mortals and that of angels. The metallic tops of the giant nodes were pushing through, and angels were flying around them, checking everything out. The angelic realm was clear and bright, with white light, highlighting the vivid colours of the angels' clothes.

So, that was how I began my efforts to turn the universe Green. If only it was as easy to fix things on Earth. But as everyone knows, Earth is a challenging place — much more so than other parts of the universe I have visited. I decided to head for home, and see how our planet was getting along. As Earth came into view, I saw an angel outside in space, holding a huge lit candle, which came up to its shoulders. The angel has ivory skin and no wings, and wore a long, white robe.

The angel moved towards a square room, hanging in space outside Earth's atmosphere. The room was like a conservatory, lined inside with mirrors. There were French windows at the front, which folded back to reveal more mirrors, like solar panels. At the back of the room, at the base, was a corrugated tube about two feet wide, like an air-conditioning hose.

The angel stood in the room holding the candle, and beckoned me to come in. I went in and rested on a ledge at the side, as I was beginning to feel tired. There were ledges around the interior of the room. Several figures in long, black robes with hoods joined me, sitting on the ledges.

'Oh look!' I thought. 'They've got outfits just like mine. Who are these beings?'

As if reading my thoughts, the angel said, 'These are Watchers. They are a high-frequency life form — much higher than you.'

This was delivered in a firm, no nonsense tone of voice. These angels are not 'airy fairy' types — just rather practical and matter of fact. They come over as kind and caring, but you wouldn't want to disagree with them!

I looked out of the room and saw five or six other mirror rooms like the one I was in. There was an angel standing in every room. The rooms began to move to a central point higher up. The six rooms moved into formation round the central point and the hoses from each room moved up to a central light and attached themselves. The general effect was like an enormous candelabra.

The six candles which the angels were holding moved into a circle around the central light. Then the whole candelabra switched on, and light began blazing from each of the rooms, magnified by the mirrors on the French windows, which were now fully open. I think the candles were being used to charge up the candelabra, because they disappeared, leaving the candelabra still blazing.

'How long will the light go on for?' I asked the angel. I was worried the batteries might not last for long.

'Forever,' the angel replied.

'Is the light to help raise the Earth's frequency?' I asked.

'Yes,' said the angel, 'That is what our work is here, raising the frequency of the universe. And we are working constantly on the Earth.'

I looked round, and became aware of several other candelabra positioned round the Earth. 'I guess they must be frequency transmitters beaming straight at Earth,' I thought.

When I looked back, I could see a long row of Watchers in their black robes and hoods, each carrying a candle, as they disappeared into the relative darkness of space.

After all that, I felt the need to get my feet on the ground. I dived into the Earth's atmosphere and landed in a dry savannah in Africa. There must have been woodland nearby, as a chimpanzee, about three feet high, strolled past, walking on arms and legs. I looked up at the sky, and checked to see if the frequency-raising lights were still there. I could see one of them, clearly visible in the background of the sky, even though it was daylight.

'Will it be seen by aircraft and space telescopes?' I thought.

As I watched, all the lights faded and became invisible. Then I figured it out. I had been operating on a higher plane than normal, which made it possible for me to see the lights. They would not be visible within our normal frequency range. When I got home, I checked the clock. My trip into space seemed like ten minutes, but it had taken two hours.

NEOLITHIC HUNTER-GATHERERS

So far, all the people I met in space who came from Earth were broadly of European and North American origin. And they were almost entirely Caucasian males. This was probably a reflection of the profile of the NATO collaboration in deep space exploration. But there was no indication, on any of the planets I visited, of our ancient ancestors. Perhaps it was unreasonable to expect that there would be, but there were trees and animals like ours on other planets — so why no indigenous humans?

I decided to go in search of original humans living on other planets. My search took me across galaxies, until I landed in a forest of trees with leaves and branches like rhododendrons. A snail, about a foot across, was climbing up one of the branches. There were a lot of crunchy, dead leaves under the trees where I was sitting. I felt them rustling close by me, and looked up to see a silvery snake heading towards me. As it moved, it kept its head and neck raised above the ground. It passed me without stopping.

Walking out of the forest, I found a clearing, where a group of five humans were clustered together. They looked like Neolithic cave people, with matted, brown hair and yellowish, light-brown complexions. They were dressed in animal skins. On the other side of the clearing, I could see a large, grey bull with huge horns, dark, woolly bison and a few tall, dappled-brown deer.

One of the men held a curved stick, with a string attached between the ends of the stick, like a bow. Taking another stick, he aimed it at one of the deer. It bounced harmlessly off the deer's hide. A woman was making a fire from dry grass, using the friction of two small sticks. She positioned four flat stones above the fire, and was intending to heat them up for cooking, when there was anything to be cooked. But there wasn't anything. Three other men stood by, watching. They all looked pretty miserable. I guess they were really hungry, because they started digging under the grass for grubs.

My previous announcements about going Green didn't seem to have reached this place. Maybe that was because the planet was in a frequency band width I hadn't visited before.

'This can't go on,' I thought, so I announced, 'Let every subatomic particle on this planet go Green, and let everyone on the planet have all my abilities.'

What happened next was surprisingly quick. Without being told, the humans almost immediately worked out how to use their minds to create what they needed. One man opened his hand like a plate, and produced a raw steak on it. He bit into it eagerly. Another man produced a cooked steak.

'Mm, this is good,' he said, as he munched through it.

Everyone had the same idea — to satisfy their hunger. Once they had done that, the man with the bow produced a much better version of the weapon in smooth wood.

'What's the point of that?' said his friend, 'We don't need to kill animals now.'

''No,' said the hunter, 'but we might need these to protect ourselves.'

Meanwhile, the woman had been making cups with liquid

in them. She handed one to each of the men.

Having made sure that the humans were no longer in difficulty, I moved my attention to the coast, where a small group of people were standing on the sandy beach. The top of the beach was dry, as if the sea never got that far up. One of the men used his mind to make a triangular, wooden hut, with an open front looking onto the sea, and with room for several people to sit comfortably inside. He went and sat inside it triumphantly. Then he made huts for everyone else.

I went back to the first group of humans I had seen. They were all standing in a line looking upwards. About ten feet above them was a row of angels with gold wings and long dark green robes.

'Do not do anything to hurt other people,' said one of the angels.

'We don't want to hurt other people,' replied the woman.

The men in her group all shook their heads in agreement. 'We are here to help you,' continued the angel.

'What a pity you weren't here before, when we really needed you,' said the woman. 'We have lived a life of suffering and desperation.'

'We couldn't come before,' another angel joined in, 'You chose to go your own way.'

"Oh no we didn't,' shouted the men.

'If I had been given a choice,' said the woman, 'I would have chosen to die. No one would want to live as we've had to.'

'You did choose,' replied the second angel. 'But it was a long time ago. You just don't remember.'

"Anyway,' continued the first angel, 'we will be with you from now on.'

I strongly sympathised with the humans' point of view. Not wanting to get involved in the wider discussion I whispered to one of the angels, 'How was it that they chose to go their own way long ago?'

'The choice was made for them by representatives of their race long ago,' explained a third angel.

'Who did that?' I asked.

'Someone higher up than us made the choice to go their own way without our help,' the third angel replied.

'Are there planets where people didn't choose to go their own way?' I said. Several angels turned to me.

'Yes, it's a major part of our work to look after people on planets from childhood onwards. In such cases, we create the babies and bring them to the planets,' explained one of them.

'Whose idea was it to make babies from humans?' I asked. The angels looked uncomfortable.

'A senior person higher up than us chose to do that.'

The conversation was getting difficult, but I felt I ought to continue. I really needed to know more about all this.

'Would it be possible for me to see a planet where the people chose to be brought up by you?' I asked.

The angels looked at each other for a moment, as though I had suggested something rather out of the ordinary. Then one of them nodded:

'Yes, we can do that. Come with us.'

So off we went. Soon we arrived at a new planet. There were soft, rolling hills and lots of green grass. On the grass I could see fifty children, all about eleven years old, playing together. A few were throwing balls to each other... or were they? Looking closer, I noticed they were using their minds to make the balls fly around.

The children were communicating telepathically. If you could tune into their wavelength, it sounded like any school playground, but they did not use their mouths to speak. The children were neither male or female. They all had long hair and pale skin, and wore long, white robes with patterns of leaves and flowers on them.

As the angels arrived, flower petals showered down on the children, and little white blobs smaller than snowflakes appeared and filled the air. It was as if the children were getting what they needed from the heavenly shower, without having to eat or drink. Or you could describe it as an upgrade. I turned to one of the angels.

'This is a much better deal than going your own way, I can see that. But why are all the children only from one race? On Earth there are many different races. Are we unique, or are there other planets with many races in other parts of the universe?'

There was a silence. Then an angel appeared holding a black baby, about a year old.

'You see, we do have them, and yes, there are other planets where they are being taken to,' said the angel.

Now I had a lot more questions in my mind.

'Look,' said the angel, 'I'm going to pass you to someone who can answer your questions better than we can.'

The angel ushered me through a door into a different environment, where another angel was waiting. This angel looked a lot different from the ones I had seen before. It was black skinned, stronger built, and wore grey-beige armour. The armour was like that worn by Roman centurions. The angel also wore a matching grey-beige helmet. But the thing I noticed most was its huge, black, bat wings. They seemed really out of place.

'Hi,' said the angel, in a friendly voice. 'I gather you want to know more about us.'

'Yes, please,' I said. 'Why are you wearing armour and a helmet. The other angels don't.' The angel pulled off its helmet, revealing a mass of black curls that extended in all directions. 'They don't like us to have our hair uncovered.'

'Who are they?' I asked, as we flew along.

'Our bosses,' the angel replied.

The angel looked so like a warrior that I asked, 'Do you have male and female genders?'

'No,' the angel replied, 'we are all the same.'

'Where are the others?' I asked.

'They are all kept separately,' said the angel. 'I am the only one that is allowed out to speak to you.'

'How come?' I said.

'There was a battle, and we were locked up,' said the angel.

'Please can you tell me what happened,' I asked.

The angel was really kind and friendly and I just couldn't believe it had done anything wrong. The angel sat down and leaned its head on its hand.

'Someone up above us put us here, to punish us, because we wouldn't fight in the battle,' the angel explained.

'Was that person bad?' I asked.

'Not bad,' said the angel, in a forgiving way, 'but someone who made bad choices.'

'What has happened to that person?' I continued.

'That person is no longer with us,' it said.

'Why didn't anyone come to free you after that?'

I had to ask, even though it felt like intruding on private

matters. The angel stepped back, opening its arms, as if to say, 'Give me a break, please…' Then it said, 'Look, I can't answer that. I just don't know why.'

'OK,' I said. 'There's another thing I want to know. Was the black race the first on planet Earth?'

"No,' the angel replied. 'The browns were first. Do you want to meet their angels?'

'Oh yes!' I said.

'Right, hold on to my hand,' the angel said, 'and I'll take you there.'

We were off in a minute, and went through a door into an area which blazed with so much light that I couldn't look at anything. I could just make out an old man with a beard sitting on a chair, flanked by statues, or maybe, they were artificial intelligence creations.

'What are you doing here?' said the old man in a cross voice.

'I am taking her to meet the browns,' said the angel.

'You can't do that!' said the old man. 'Now get back inside your area.'

I was incensed. This guy was supposed to be in charge of angels, but he obviously was the wrong man for the job.

'That's not very loving, is it?' I shouted.

The old man shrugged his shoulders with an air of resignation. 'Oh, all right,' he said. 'Take her across, but come straight back.'

The angel took my hand once more, and led me through the area of blazing light, to the portal leading to the browns area.

'Thanks,' it said as it left.

'See you soon,' I replied, and I stepped through the portal.

The scene changed completely. I was on the side of a green hill with a few scattered trees. Floating round me there were people with brown skin and long, dark hair, wearing long, brown robes. On Earth they would be described as Asian. They held long brown pieces of material that flowed out behind them like cloaks. They were everywhere, far too many of them for the area they were in. In the middle of the area was a tall, shiny artificial intelligence statue, standing guard.

'What is your business here?' said the statue in a strangely artificial voice. I didn't need to hear any more.

'These people may be angels, but they are in captivity,' I thought. 'Something is awfully wrong here.'

Then I said, 'Let every subatomic particle in the universe go Green,' and waited to see what would happen.

The artificial intelligence statue made a strange noise and sank into the ground. All the portals and environments I had been through, disappeared, and the brown angels just floated quietly out into the darkness of space.

I raced back to find the black angel, but it had disappeared too, so tuning into its frequency, I followed after it. Then I was on another planet with a lot of tall trees. I could see a lot of a black angels perched in the tops of the trees. They were crouched down, concerned in case their appearance might frighten anyone who didn't know who they were. I was pleased to see that their armour had gone, but they still had bat wings. I suspected that the planet needed to go Green, so I changed it.

As soon as the planet went Green, the black angels came down from the trees and started altering their appearance to how they wanted to be. Now they had silver-feathered wings and long dark robes. Across the valley I could see brown angels changing as well. They had chosen cream-coloured feathers for their wings.

'Why were good angels being held in captivity?' I thought.

Nothing made sense to me. So I began climbing up to the top of the universe again. This time, as I reached the place where I could see daylight, a hand reached down and helped me up. I was standing on a pleasant patio, with white metal chairs round a table, inside a birdcage gazebo. A white angel with a long white robe, was sitting opposite me.

'Sit down,' said the angel. 'What do you want to know?'

'What was the war in heaven about?' I asked

'A member of the Senior Counsellors decided to create people in the universe with two genders, and to control everything that happened in the universe,' the angel said. 'That took away the angels' role of bringing babies to planets and looking after them.'

'Who are the Senior Counsellors?' I continued.

'They are not angels. They have a form like humans, and they decide how impulses that come from the heart of existence should take form in the universe,' the angel explained.

'Why were good angels locked up, when they had done nothing wrong?' I asked.

'They chose not to obey their commander, so their commander ordered them to be put in prison,' the angel replied.

'But if I understand it correctly,' I continued, 'their commander was acting contrary to the heavenly code.'

'Yes,' said the angel, 'But angels have to obey orders.'

"What if the orders are wrong?' I asked.

At this point, the black angel I met before re-appeared and sat down at the table, with a cup of coffee. It now had little, gold wings like epaulettes on each shoulder, as well as bigger wings at the back.

'There were no rules about that, as it never happened before,' explained the black angel, dunking a biscuit in the coffee.

'So what made you decide not to obey your commander's orders?' I asked.

'You see,' continued the black angel, resting its feet on the coffee table, 'this guy wanted to control the universe, and run everything. Now, to me, that seemed wrong. So I decided not to fight for that.'

'Didn't this guy have a boss further up?' I asked.

'Oh yes,' said the angel, 'That high up guy was really evil. That was the one behind it all.'

"What happened to the evil one?' I questioned.

'The other high-ups poured their energy on that one, and it was forced out of the universe and down far below.'

'Which angels did your commander fight against?'

'Several phalanxes of angels. They were higher ranking ones.'

"Then your commander was bound to lose.'

'Yes,' the angel nodded, stirring the coffee.

He seemed to be hinting that he had had enough questions, as he picked up a newspaper, and started reading it.

'If you were a conscientious objector, you shouldn't have been locked up,' I persisted.

'The jailers had no choice but to obey their commander's orders,' explained the angel, peering round the newspaper.

'Why didn't anyone come and free you, since you were

wrongly imprisoned?'

''It just got overlooked,' replied the angel, smiling.

I began to suspect that racial discrimination had taken place.

'Are black and brown angels represented at all levels in heaven?' I asked.

'Would you like a word with my boss about that?' the angel said, laughing. A great black angel with golden wings came flying over.

'Come with me,' it said. 'We have all types of angels. I would take you to see brown angels,' it continued, 'but they can be a bit feisty — so better stick with me,' it added, laughing.

One thing I soon learned about black angels — they have a great sense of humour, and they love to mimic our Earthly ways, such as drinking coffee. They do it to show that they care about us humans, and know all the details of our lives. As we flew along, I asked the great angel, 'Was the evil commander only in charge of black and brown angels?'

'Oh no, far, from it,' replied the great angel. 'The majority of angels that rebelled were white. They are still in prison. The brown and black angels had better judgment, but just a few of them were unlucky enough to be under the bad guy's command.'

'So,' I thought, 'they would have gone to prison if they had supported the bad guy, but because they chose not to, they still went to prison for disobeying their commander's orders.'

We went to a lovely planet where scores of small, black children aged three and four years old were running about playing on grassy hillocks. They had beautiful tops and trousers which were white with coloured, flower patterns, and their hair was braided and tied in various ways. The great angel brought me a young baby, two months old. It cradled the baby in its arms, looking down at it, and looking up at me, as if to say, 'Go on, you've got to admit this baby is the cutest ever.'

A four-year-old child appeared, pushing a buggy for the new baby.

'See,' said the black angel, 'we look after every child, from the moment of its birth throughout its life. These babies are born from the womb of nothingness and as they materialise, we take charge of them. They grow up and experience life in the universe, and when they are ready, they go to join all the people in heaven. They do not have to grow old or die.'

'Why don't the babies have wings like angels?' I asked.

'There are human-looking people up there, called counsellors, who have a say in what the babies look like, but we angels get to choose most of the details, so we all choose what we like best,' the angel said.

'Do you choose the colours of the babies?' I asked.

'The babies will be the colour of the angels who are looking after them,' explained the great angel. 'But we choose our own colours.'

Then, as if reading my mind, it added, 'We choose black, because we prefer to look like this.'

The great angel gave me a look of infinite patience and understanding, that showed it knew all about the trials faced by people of different races on Earth.

ABOVE THE UNIVERSE

I thanked the great black angel and went off to try and make sense of what I had been told. From what the angels had shown me, I could see how life might work if there had been no evil. But why had there been evil, and why had parts of the universe had been affected, including the Earth?

Without out realising it, I had already gone up into a high frequency area where it was daylight. But I was stopped from going any further by a 'glass ceiling.' I looked up at the ceiling and started shouting, 'WHY? WHY? WHY?'

There was a loud noise like a vacuum cleaner, and a golden tube came down through the glass ceiling. Another one that was wider came down and fitted over it. The tube kept on widening until it

was about ten feet in diameter. A door in the tube flew open, displaying a golden lift. I got in, and the door closed. Then we were going up. Eventually, the lift stopped, and the door flew open again. I stepped out into a domed, stone courtyard. Through the stone gateway I could see a wonderfully uplifting light outside, and the silhouette of a tree.

I wanted to look at everything out there, but it was rather too bright. Two angels, black and brown, appeared carrying an ornate headdress covered with precious stones. They fitted it over my head. There were glass sections for my eyes. The headdress became invisible, but it was doing its job, making me able to see and hear things which were really too high frequency for me.

I moved towards the garden. The tree was more like a sculpture than a tree, with leaves that seemed to have a ceramic consistency. Some leaves pointed up into the air, and grew directly on the branches, not on twigs. There was a sound like bird song.

'It's probably my imagination,' I thought, but then a large blackbird landed heavily on one of the branches.

At that moment, a tall, saintly person in a long, dark velvet robe appeared. It had a senior appearance, with short, grey hair, and features that on Earth we would describe as slightly feminine.

'You have questions,' the saintly person said, in a friendly way. 'If you would like to come up to my room I will explain.'

The being, whose name was Treto, went up a stone, spiral, turret staircase that led to a room on the floor above. I knew I wouldn't be able to go up higher on my own, but as Treto walked up the stairs, it pointed to a small, golden lift next to the stairs. I got in gratefully. Soon I was in a circular room with stone walls. It had the feel of an old castle.

Treto was sitting on a stone bench, with a stone table in front of it. The table was covered with plain, white paper.

'Sit down,' said Treto, pointing to a stone stool.

'You want to know how evil came into the universe, don't you?' I nodded.

Treto took up a dark pencil and drew a large circle on the paper. 'Would you agree that the universe is part of All That Is?' asked Treto.

'Yes,' I said.

Over the last few months, I had come to realise that the

universe is only part of All That Is, and there is a whole lot more going on, that happens outside it.

'Well,' continued Treto, 'to be "All That Is" means including the possibility of everything, nothing left out.'

I nodded. Treto drew a small black dot in the circle.

'This dot represents the possibility of evil happening,' Treto said. 'Of course, it is only one possibility out of an infinite number, but it exists.'

'OK,' I said.

'So,' said Treto, 'sooner or later, that possibility of evil existing might come to fruition, and in fact it did, with harmful consequences.'

'But,' Treto went on, 'if everyone in the universe were to choose not to have the possibility of evil, you would get this.'

Treto drew a circle without a black dot.

'If that happened, would all beings in the universe be able to live together without danger from others?' I asked.

I was thinking of animals that have to kill others just in order to live.

'Yes,' said Treto. 'When that happens, no species will be allowed to steal the life of another species in order to carry on its own subsistence.'

'I can't imagine that ever happening,' I thought, 'How long do we have to wait for that?'

"It's like this,' said Treto, drawing a big oval. 'This is the universe.'

Treto drew a black dot in the middle of the universe, and another one at a point on the edge of the universe.

'You are here,' said Treto, pointing to the dot in the middle, 'and, you are also out here,' pointing to the dot on the edge of the universe.

'I am in both places at once?' I asked.

'Yes,' said Treto. 'At the centre, you experience everything at once. But at the spot on the edge, your experience is limited.'

'But doesn't that remove your individuality at the centre?' I asked.

'Only at a higher level,' said Treto. 'At the centre, I am everyone. I can, if I wish, experience all of this at the centre. But my particular work is here.'

'So are you saying that from the central perspective, the bad things have stopped, but that at the perimeter, I can experience them as still happening?'

'At the centre, bad things cannot happen, but at the perimeter, they can, until everything in existence chooses to have the possibility of bad things removed,' Treto continued.

I could not get my head round that, but I said nothing.

'The person of Lucifer, a high spirit, *7 was removed,' Treto continued, 'but it left universal programmes to carry out its plans, which, from our perspective are still in operation, even though it is locked up. So that is where we are now. But one day, even Lucifer and the others that rebelled and are locked up, will chose to live where the possibility of bad things cannot happen.'

'If I am at the centre, does it feel as if everything is over, and the universe has finished?' I asked.

At that moment, a gatekeeper in charge of an entry portal into heaven, the place where evil does not exist, looked down and said, 'No, it's not as simple as that. We have a role to play.'

Treto looked up.

'Can you come and explain?'

'No,' said the gatekeeper, 'I do not have time now. Too

many people are waiting for entry through this gate at the moment. I just wanted to say that if the universe comes to an end, we have a role in closing it down. After that, we retreat into the formless realm where we come from. But that cannot happen until everything in the universe has chosen not to have the possibility of evil.'

'What about heaven?' I thought. 'Will that close down too?'

'It cannot be discussed,' said the gatekeeper. 'There are realms above heaven, but to your perception, they are formless.'

The gatekeeper withdrew, and I returned to my conversation with Treto. 'Am I right in thinking that there are no genders in heaven?'

'Yes,' said Treto.

'Then,' I continued, 'how do you refer to someone in the third person? We say "he, she or it". What do you say?'

'We say "they" for both singular and plural,' Treto replied, 'Just like "you" which can be both singular or plural.'

So now I had my answer. But saying 'they' sounded weird, so I decided to go on using 'it' for the singular when applied to angels and higher beings.

Treto spoke again. 'The higher humans had a role in designing the shape of humans on Earth, but higher humans have no gender. Lucifer knew that having two genders wouldn't work in the longer term, but it wanted to populate the Earth quickly, so it chose that method.'

Somehow, we were out in the wonderful garden now, where the sky glowed with the light of dawn. 'That's how it is in heaven,' said Treto, looking around.

Then it pointed upwards. I looked up. There was a cloud

barrier like a ceiling above us.

'I can't take you up there,' said Treto, 'or you wouldn't be able to come back. But don't worry about that now. Before you go, I have a gift for you.'

Treto went over to a tree, and taking a leaf, turned it into a pendant on a chain. It pressed the pendant into my hand.

I was immensely pleased to be given such a beautiful present, and put it over my head immediately. I was even happier, now that so many things had been explained to me. Thanking Treto for everything, I descended into the lower levels below.

The white angel in the white robe was still sitting alone in the bird cage gazebo. 'Did you ever go to heaven?' I asked.

The angel looked at me hesitantly.

'Only once or twice on official business,' it said.

'But people say that humans can go there when they die.' I continued. The white angel nodded its head humbly.

'I have heard about it.'

I thought it was rather hard that there was one law for humans and another for angels. I wanted the white angel to share the experience I just had with Treto. So I tuned into the frequency of my new pendant, and offered an identical frequency experience to the angel. The next thing I saw was the feet of the angel floating upwards.

'Thank you, I am free now,' it said.

The angel came from a lower order which did not have free access to heaven, and after the upgrade, it was able to go there at will. Although I didn't fully understand what had just happened, I thought I should offer the same thing to any angels in the universe that had missed out. Holding on to my leaf pendant I connected with the universal computer, and said:

'Let all angelic beings everywhere in the universe now have access to this frequency.'

As I descended back down into the universe, and into the shadows of space, I caught sight of angels here and there, some black, some brown and some white. They all looked marvellous as usual, but something was different about them... Suddenly I knew what it was. They all had glowing halos round their heads, just like angels that you see in mediaeval and Renaissance paintings. I expect that higher angels all have halos, but so far, the great black angel was the only one I had seen with a halo.

As I headed for Earth, I saw the Earth angel and a group of Watchers all standing there. The angel now had a bright halo, and the Watchers had discreet paler ones. When they saw me, they all started clapping their hands and smiling, as if to say 'thank you.'

BELOW THE UNIVERSE

As I got closer to Earth, I started thinking again about what a bad deal a few unlucky angels got when the war in heaven was over. Because they had the rebel angel as their commander, they had to fight on its side, or be put in prison for disobeying orders. But if they obeyed orders, and fought on the wrong side, they were punished with what looked like a worse prison, forever, far below, outside the universe.

Humans have a strong sense of justice. No one teaches kids to say, 'It's not fair!'

They are just born like that. Being human, I wanted to help any angels who might have done nothing wrong, but who might be down there, just because they were in the wrong place at the wrong time. Clutching my leaf pendant, I tuned into the universe computer, and asked to go where any trapped angels might be.

I arrived in an area of shadows. There was a dark cloud barrier below me, and I went through it. I could see an opening in the dark, and looked inside. There were cages — just cages, and nothing else. In the dark, I could dimly see the enormous limbs of giant angels lying on the ground. A terrible noise came out of the opening. It was like a roaring howling sound. You could tell from that noise that the inmates were deeply troubled.

As my eyes got used to the dark, I could make out smaller

cages. Each cage had a white angel in it. Angels do not suffer hunger, thirst or pain as we do. It is all about their mental state. The angels in the smaller cages were not howling or in torment. They sat peacefully, without complaint, accepting their fate. It was time to act. Focusing on the interior of the prison opening I said 'Let everyone and everything in there that needs to go Green, go Green!.'

Immediately, five angels floated out of their cages, through the prison opening, and up towards the dark cloud barrier. Angels above the cloud barrier reached down with their arms, and pulled the ascending angels out. I followed them upwards. More angels were coming to help. They put their arms around the freed angels to aid them as they made their way further and further upwards. Eventually, I lost sight of them.

As I returned to Earth, I could hear terrorists talking about what I had learned from Treto. They weren't able to follow me into space, but they were listening to my thoughts.

'So that explains it,' said one Irish terrorist. 'Inside heaven, everyone has mentally voted to exclude the possibility of evil. But outside heaven, you can't expect the universe to be fair or treat people equally, because it has to include all possibilities. That is why some angels got a worse deal than others, it was just their bad luck.'

I hadn't really grasped that point, but this terrorist had understood everything.

So far, I hadn't met any fallen angels. But all that changed, when I got back to Earth, and a group of strange-looking terrorists attacked me in my garden. These guys were dressed in Italian Renaissance-style clothing. They had short, mustard-coloured jackets, clinched at the waist, with short pleats below it. They wore dark-grey leggings and flat hats made of velvet with a feather in them. They had been brought in to my garden under a criminal intergalactic agreement, because the terrorists on Earth were temporarily running short of staff, and had to call on people off-planet as a last resort. As usual, I removed the intruders, and tuned into the place they came from.

They were living on a planet with pleasant green hills and attractive Italian villas made of stone and bricks, with arched windows, high ceilings and supporting pillars. Roses were trained against the outside of the buildings. When I arrived on their planet, Renaissance men were lounging on a bank outside a villa. I went up and asked one of them whether they were from Earth.

'Yes, but we have lived here for a long time,' said one of them, whose name was Pittarus. 'We came here to set up our new colony outside Earth.'

'How did you get here?' I asked

'We have friends in high places,' said Pittarus, pointing upwards.

I looked up and saw a grey fallen angel, with mottled grey and charcoal wings, hovering further up the hill.

'They created pathways for us long ago, and we came in that way. I suppose we could go back to Earth, but we have a better life, here,' Pittarus said.

I looked for a pathway, and saw a shimmering tunnel against the skyline. It looked like a 'wormhole' to me. It must have been created when the fallen angels were still at large, before they were expelled from heaven and lost all their power.

'They don't just want to control Earth,' continued Pittarus proudly. 'They want to run the whole universe.'

'How are they doing so far?' I asked.

'I can't say how much success they have had on that,' Pittarus admitted. 'They fell from their country, higher up, and want to rebuild their city on Earth. They go to Earth, but not very often.'

'Did they create these buildings?' I continued.

'No,' said Pittarus, 'but they showed us how to do it. They can't operate in our physical environment.'

'So,' I thought, 'they've lost all their power. They need a labour-force and they've stolen men from Earth to work for them.'

'They can take physical form if they want to,' said Pittarus, pointing to several young men standing nearby.

A group of sulky, young men, with Roman hair-styles and long Roman robes, were standing talking nearby, looking rather self-conscious. Nearby, and not at all self-conscious, another young man lifted up his robe and started pleasuring himself loudly. Two other young men came to assist him. The scene was similar to that of a Roman mural in a brothel from Pompeii. I wondered if the wormhole had been designed to take the fallen angels straight to some part of the red light district in Ancient Rome.

Another group of young men appeared. They had furtive sideways glances, and sneering expressions, as if sharing a joke at someone else's expense. One of them walked over to us, and I immediately disappeared.

'Who were you talking to?' asked the young man, suspiciously.

'She's disappeared,' said Pittarus.

'It can't be a she!' cried the young man. 'It's her! She's been here. We must escape.'

Using a command, I announced, 'Select all fallen angels,

both winged and un-winged, and send them to the terrorists' targeting board!'

The targeting board is a computer screen, where biodata of recently identified, targeted individuals, is held. It is accessible to all terrorists who want to earn quick money. All they have to do is to log on, and select a person to target. That person is downloaded to their local computer, from where they can inflict various attacks via WiFi. The system records their activities, and allocates money to their bank account.

Suddenly all the fallen angels were on the targeting board.

'And let all Renaissance human beings on this planet receive the same targeting attacks as I do from now on,' I added.

Back on Earth, two junior terrorists in Connecticut were looking for work. They logged on to the targeting board, and scrolled down the list of individuals. They clicked on one, and the real-time live-streaming image of a winged angel came into view. They stared at the angel for a minute.

'Hey, look at that!'

'What do you think it is?'

'Don't know. Look at its legs, there are wings on them.'

'Are you sure they're not boots?'

'No, definitely wings.'

'Let's see if I can take this one out.'

The operative clicked on a drop-down box and selected from a choice of attacks on body parts. He selected the bladder and hit 'Fire.'

'I think I hit him!' cried the operative.

The fallen angel was hovering under a tree, wings outspread. Suddenly, he cried out and landed on the ground, falling backwards. He examined his sullied robe.

'It's disgusting! It never happened to me before! I want to go to the US military. They will protect me.'

'What a coward!' I thought.

'Let me have a go,' said the other operative, studying the drop-down box. He activated an attack.

'Yes! I hit him right in the genitals!'

By now, the fallen angel was lying on its back, staring into space, having a philosophical moment. 'What is this terrible pain I am experiencing, in parts of me I forgot existed?'*8

The operatives tried again, aiming for the head this time.

'By my faith,' cried the fallen angel, 'they are invisible. I can't see them anywhere.'

Soon there were fallen angels lying on the ground all over the planet. At that moment, one of the Renaissance men walked by.

'What are you doing lying on the ground?' he asked a fallen angel.

'I've been hit by those people of yours,' the fallen angel replied.

'What a fuss,' said the Italian, 'You've got wings, fly yourself up!'

At that moment, I was attacked by a ghoul in my garden, and the Renaissance man, now linked to me, fell to the ground.

'You see,' said the fallen angel, 'now you're caught too. It's that woman on Earth who hacked us into herself. She is causing all this trouble.'

It was all too much for one fallen Angel. His larynx was targeted by a junior US terrorist, and he started coughing.

'My breath is coming in fits and starts, I cannot stand it,' he cried.

He sat up, his arm around a tree trunk and started weeping.

'If only I had stayed in my home Kingdom. *I want to go to the United States.*'

'Going to the United States' was a formula I had created to help victims of terrorism on Earth who were seeking asylum. It took them straight to the US Military. It became well-known, not only on Earth but on other planets, as the escape route of last resort.

No sooner had the fallen angel said the magic formula, than he was flying into the US ghouls' portal in New York. The US portal guards looked rather startled.

'Not my problem,' I thought, 'Try repatriating that one!'

RUFFIANS REUNITED

Back on Earth, the terrorists had been discussing developments on the planet of the ruffians with interest, because the ruffians had come from their own community. These older men, known to them affectionately as 'Pops,' were poor people who had fallen on hard times in the 1980s, got into debt and were forced to work for the Mafia. Their US Mafia bosses had sold the Pops as slaves to the Boston Planet, when they got too old to be useful to them.

The terrorists clustered round their fMRI screens, linked by WiFi to an fMRI machine in their central office. The fMRI screens interpreted and recorded video images of what was in my mind when I was talking to the rescued ruffians. Using special adaptations developed by the US Mafia's technical support group, they watched me talking to the rescued ruffians, and recognised them.

Word got around, and soon, seven other 'Pops' men were asking if they could see the video too. They watched Rob, Tom and Con, the freed men, looking fit and well, enjoying a life without cares in a pleasant, natural landscape. As they watched, they saw more men come over the hill on the ruffians planet.

'Look, there's Joe!' cried one of them, 'I remember him!'

"Why didn't I get the chance to go?' another complained.

'There's nothing stopping you,' I pointed out. 'I gave

everyone on Earth the same abilities that I have, over a year ago.'

'Oh! We didn't know that,' said the Pops.

'I want to go and be with my mates,' one of them whispered. A moment later, he appeared there. Rob and Tom were sitting on boulders doing nothing in particular when he appeared. Rob did a double take.

'Tom, I think we've got another one arrived!' he said. Tom looked up. The new arrival waved at the men.

'Hello, you remember me, don't you?'

'Oh, it's not old Walt, is it?' Tom called.

The two men ambled towards each other, and Tom patted Walt on the back. 'Welcome, welcome, old chap,' he murmured, as Walt wiped a tear from his eye.

What Walt had not known was that the moment he set foot on the planet, he was changed by the Green effect. Now, he not only had the cleverest brain in the universe, but perfect health and a lot more besides, because of the recent heaven-leaf upgrade. This was too much for the six Pops watching the video, and they all arrived at once. Other men already on the planet began to gather round, calling out to their friends. 'Look who's here! Come and see!'

The new arrivals quickly got used to their new home.

'Are there any more men like that left alive anywhere?' I thought. I tuned into the universal computer and said, 'Let any men like the Pops in existence now go Green and arrive here.'

A further seven elderly men appeared. I explained to them what had happened, and asked them to take a look round the planet and see if they wanted to stay.

'Can we go back to Earth if we want to?' one of them asked.

'Sure,' I said, 'you can go anytime. But do you have a safe place where you can go?'

They admitted that they didn't at the moment. All the men decided they would stay and give the planet a try. Meanwhile, Walt, the first one to arrive, was starting to settle in.

'Can I make myself a hut?' he asked.

'Feel free,' said Rob.

Two huts appeared, and a few men went inside. Others started exploring the rocky hills nearby. Walt came over to me. He had cheered up a lot since his arrival.

'Can we live here forever?' he asked.

'There's no reason why not,' I replied, 'You need never grow old here. You can make your body whatever age you want.'

'Will there be no death then?' Con asked.

Sensing a teaching opportunity, a white angel appeared and stood about five feet above the ground.

'You do not need to die of sickness or old age any more,' it announced. 'But when the time comes, you will feel ready to go to the heavenly realms above. All you have to do is to ask to be taken up there, and you will be taken.'

'I feel ready now,' said Walt, standing up confidently.

It was not clear if he had fully understood what the angel was saying, but he was volunteering anyway.

'If you are ready, go right ahead,' the angel said.

Walt looked up into the sky and disappeared. I followed him, mainly out of curiosity, as I knew he would be all right. Walt made it straight up into the foothills of the heavenly realm. Treto came out to meet him.

'Hello,' it said, 'I know why you've come.' It put its hand on Walt's shoulder.

'You're not ready to go up there yet. But one day you will be. Here, take this. It will remind you what to do when that day comes.'

Just as it had done for me, Treto pulled a leaf from a heavenly tree, hung it on a chain, and put the chain over Walt's head. Walt thanked Treto and came back down again. The other men heard about everything that happened to him, and felt satisfied with what the angel told them about living forever.

'Can you give me a leaf chain like yours?' Con asked Walt.

Walt made all the men on the planet chains like his, so that they would remember what to do when the time came.

'I wish we had angels like that to explain everything to us on Earth,' I thought as I left.

But I knew that things on Earth are a lot different from most other places I had visited. When I got back, several ghoul supervisors were hanging around like sharks, waiting to talk to me. They had been watching what happened, using fMRI screens, and wanted to turn heaven into a trafficking opportunity, which they could control by charging money for access to it. They started hinting what a chance it would be for them to go on an exciting trip up to heavenly places.

'Go ahead, nothing's stopping you,' I replied.

But strangely enough, none of them fancied their chances of making it up there.

ARTURUS SUPER SOLDIERS

In chapters six and seven, I met a group of children on the commercial space station where Natt and Abe worked, not far from Earth. Abe told me the children had been born off-planet, and were now preparing to return to Earth. But if so, where were their parents? Abe also said that the children were going to live in a secure, military compound until they got used to their environment. But as I was leaving, I head Abe whisper to Natt, 'What else could I do? I had to say something.'

So maybe I hadn't been given the full story, or even the right story. It still bothered me. Tuning into the universe computer system, I said, 'I want to know where those children come from.'

Immediately I was on a large commercial mothership. It was bright and airy, with artificial, full-spectrum lighting, giving the feeling that you were outdoors. Small two-year-old children were toddling about everywhere. They were coming out of a large, dark, domed room, which had the feel of an indoor chicken run full of young chicks. There must have been fifty of them.

A man and woman wearing white lab coats were in the outer area, talking to a well-dressed business woman. The business woman was carrying one of the children in her arms.

'We'll take this one for now and do tests on it,' she said. 'Then we'll be in touch.' She left, still carrying the child.

'I want to see where the children are born,' I thought.

A vast laboratory full of water tanks came into view. Inside each water tank, there was an unborn child. The children were broadly all at the same stage of development. At the end of the laboratory there was a glass-walled office, with two senior scientists in white coats standing inside.

'Ours are ten to fifteen percent more intelligent than those of our competitors,' said the scientist in charge of operations. 'We supply all planets occupied by our people across the galaxy, and ten percent of our output goes to the home market.'

What he meant was that his business involved supplying children as a labour force on planets where Earth people were living, and that ten per cent of the children went to the Earth itself. If that was true, that would explain what those children were doing with Abe and Natt, on the space station near Earth. They were to be delivered to private clients on our planet.

The scientist in charge handed a sheaf of statistical printouts to the other scientist, who represented a group of potential clients.

'You can check these when you get back,' he added, 'You will see that our children consistently out-perform the official standards.'

'So,' I thought, 'they are basically in the child farming business.'

I remembered Natt, and how he felt, because he didn't know where he came from, or where the rest of his people were.

'What must it be like, if you are just another number in a laboratory batch, and no one takes the trouble to explain who your parents were?' I thought.

'I want to see what happens to the children, and what

people are driving this process,' I announced.

The laboratory faded out, and I was on a planet with a landscape of smooth, green hills. The planet's name was Arturus. A group of tall young soldiers in pale camouflage uniforms were training in unarmed combat techniques. As the sergeant gave the order, two men raced towards each other. They braced arms in confrontation, and one of the men, pushing on the other's shoulders, sailed up into the air, leapfrogging over his opponent. The other soldiers, who were watching, applauded. The sergeant gave the order for the next pair of men to begin. They ran towards each other, and this time, the man coming from the other direction somersaulted over his opponent's shoulders.

When all the men had taken a turn, they lined up, and the sergeant approached each one and aimed a punch at them. But none of them got hit. Instead, they all fell to the ground before they could be hit, with precision timing, designed to counter an enemy attacker. These were super soldiers, with genetically enhanced physiology, learning unorthodox, ground-based skills.

Then their sergeant handed out metal headbands which fitted around their heads. The sergeant operated equipment transmitting electrical impulses remotely through the soldiers' skulls to their brains. The men shifted from side to side as if dancing in formation, ducking and weaving.

I have seen this technology operated by North Koreans, and in that case, it was used unethically, treating men like bridled horses, led by their heads, using electronic shock treatment. But this time, the young soldiers were not subjected to pain. Retaining invisibility, I mentally prompted the sergeant to explain what he was doing. He did not realise I was there, but his mind responded automatically.

'The technology helps soldiers coordinate their movements. They develop a group mind-set,' he said. 'That way, they all look out for each other like brothers.'

Once the training session was over, the men removed the cranial circuits, and went off to their canteen for lunch.

'So, perhaps those children I saw will end up as soldiers,' I thought. 'I wonder who is behind the intergalactic child production business.'

The scene changed. I was in a palatial office suite furnished in stained oak, with oak panels below window-level all round. The view from the windows was of a natural landscape, with trees and green hills stretching towards fields lined with low hedges.

Looking out on this landscape from his chief executive desk was a man in his early sixties. His name was Sir Joseph Turner. He had received his British knighthood for services to industry in the field of military technologies, but most of his Earth-based business interests were in North American mining. He was tall, with broad shoulders, and was impeccably dressed in a brown, tweed suit. Standing opposite him, also dressed in brown tweed, was the vice chairman, a man slightly younger and thinner than his boss, who came from the US.

'I have everything I want here,' Sir Joseph said, as he gazed across the fields. 'If things ever get difficult, we can always fly back to Earth.'

'Oh, certainly,' said the vice chairman, 'but I hope that won't happen just yet.' At that moment, a smart-looking woman came in.

'Your visitors have arrived,' she announced.

Two men with briefcases stood at the door, wearing beige raincoats. They had come from a vast mothership, not far off, and arrived on the planet by scout ship.

'Ah yes, of course,' said the chairman, 'Do come through, gentlemen,' and he led them into the adjoining oak-panelled meeting room.

No sooner had they all sat down, than the chief visitor turned to the chairman and said, 'Let's get to the point, Sir Joseph. We have a hundred thousand men out there. You only have ten thousand. It's a takeover!'

The two visitors looked expectantly at their hosts, anticipating that they would immediately surrender. But they had misread the situation.

'Don't be so silly, man,' Sir Joseph replied. 'Every one of ours is worth ten of yours. You'd lose if you took us on.'

Turning to the vice chairman, he added, 'Why don't we all go for lunch.'

At this, the two visitors put their hands inside their coats, and drawing out two handguns, shot the unfortunate chairman and his deputy. Sir Joseph died instantly, but the vice chairman had just enough strength to hit the emergence button under the table, before he passed out. Immediately, sirens started shrieking, and the sound of metal portcullis gates coming down could be heard around the building.

'Quick, run for it!' shouted the chief.

The two men dashed for the stairs, avoiding the lift, guns in hand.

As they got to the bottom, they were met by twenty super-soldiers armed with rifles, who swiftly annihilated them. The base's military commander stepped forward to examine the bodies. A scout ship came into view and tried to land to collect the two murderers, but it was hit with close range missiles, and burst into flames. The commander and his two lieutenant commanders, Frank and Reese, sat in the foyer of the vast company building discussing tactics.

'The mothership won't come within range of our missiles,' said Reese.

'No, but it's not likely to go away, either,' replied Frank.

'We'll have to go up there and finish them off,' said the commander. 'Of course, they'll be expecting us, so we'll have to work out a way round that.'

'We can go up at night,' said Frank, 'but they will detect us once we're in range, even if we use scouts with stealth modifications.'

'How about…' said the commander, thinking as he spoke, 'how about, we leave from the other side of the planet, head off, and come back up above the ship. They won't be expecting us to land on the roof. If we go now, we can wait there, out of range until the last minute.'

And that is what they did. They still ran a risk of being detected, but they took all possible measures to remain undiscovered. There were no ground-to-air communications. The commander stayed down, but Frank and Reese each led a group of ten scouts into position.

Finally, after dark, it was time to move. The first group of scouts, led by Reese, came into range. Fifty men swiftly descended on ropes down onto different parts of the roof of the vast mother ship. The second group of scouts stayed back, ready to rescue the others if things went wrong.

The men on the ship's roof raced to plant mines where they would do most damage. They had nearly finished, when their enemies inside realised what was happening. Windows began opening in the roof.

'Back! Back! Everyone off the ship!' Reese shouted over the intercom system.

Now that their presence had been discovered, there was no further point in keeping out of contact. Reese's scout ships moved closer to the mothership. This was the moment of greatest danger, as the men held onto ropes and were winched up into the scouts. By now, their enemies were on the roof in their hundreds, firing at the scouts. Large guns were being deployed upwards.

Reese checked that all his men were off the roof. 'Go! Go!' he shouted to the pilots.

A few of his men were still being winched up, as the scouts took off at speed. Frank's scouts, still out of range, prepared to take on the enemy with missiles, if all else failed. The risk was that they

might all be blown apart when the mothership went up, if they didn't clear the area in time. Frank was monitoring the distance that Reese's scouts were from the mothership. By now, their enemies knew exactly where they all were and missiles were firing in all directions. The scouts were programmed to dodge the missiles, but in doing so, the men inside were being flung from side to side.

Frank kept his eye on the distance between Reese's scouts and the mothership, but it was getting tricky for them, dodging the missiles.

'Hit them now Frank!' Reese called urgently on the intercom. 'Don't wait for us, or you'll get caught!' Frank held his nerve as long as he could, then he gave the order. 'Fire! Fire!'

As he spoke, the operators hit the mines' ignition. There

was a silence which seemed to last forever. Then the mines on the roof of the mothership began to detonate. The scouts were racing away as fast as they could. One of Reese's ships was winged, and began plunging towards Arturus. The men bailed out in spacesuits and parachutes.

Frank ordered his scout ship back towards them. A large net shot out of his ship, picking up the survivors, and reeling them in fast, as the scout shot off again. Then the first explosions began. The mothership roof was blown, taking the missile launchers with it, so there was no immediate danger, provided the scouts could get far enough away. The second wave of explosions began, as the scouts hurtled out of the area.

At last! They were clear. The scouts could afford to slow down enough to watch. There was an enormous explosion, lighting up space for miles around, followed by two more, and the mothership went blazing red. Then the white heat on the inside was exposed, and as if in slow motion, the ship began to break up. The prow flew upwards, other parts broke apart, and then the loudest explosion of all, accompanied by red and grey smoke clouds, broke the darkness of space. It was over.

Reese and Frank breathed a sigh of relief. Reese got on the intercom to Frank. 'Home, I think!' he called.

'Yup, see you there,' replied Frank, and the entire fleet of ships turned and headed back to safety.

THE BIG PLAN FOR EARTH

After the space battle, I went home. It seemed that parts of the universe were like the 'Wild West.' You needed a good army to survive, and there were plenty of law-breakers out there.

It was clear that child farming was big business within the galaxy. For all I knew, it might even be legal, as how else were civilisations on other planets to develop without a work force? Using people from Earth was not an option, given the secrecy surrounding the deep space programme. But there were serious ethical considerations about mass-production of 'test-tube' babies. Would the children be given to good homes, or would they be treated as slaves? And who, if anyone, was regulating these operations?

Another thing which puzzled me was why ten per cent of the child farming output was going back to Earth? We have plenty of people here already. I decided to tune into the universe computer and ask to see where the children destined for Earth were going.

Immediately, I was back on a space station close to Earth. A group of twenty young toddlers were wandering around. Two space station staff were encouraging them to toddle into an empty room, where they were herded into a playpen. The doors were locked on the outside. A light source switched on inside the room, and the children started to shimmer inside the light beam. Then they disappeared. I guessed they were being 'beamed' down to an Earth location.

I followed the children down to Earth, and found myself in a private underground base on the Mexican side of the US border. I was in a room with large, double doors. The doors opened automatically, and the twenty toddlers, now released from the play pen, came into view, walking somewhat unsteadily. They crossed the room, and went into a patio area, which led out onto a sunny garden. Several nurses in uniform came forward to help and reassure the children. The nurses checked all the children to make sure they were all right.

'Nothing serious,' announced the senior nurse. 'Just a few bumps and bruises.'

The children had never been on a planet before, and it would take a few days for them to get used to the Earth's gravity and day and night cycles. They had never seen grass either, and they naturally gravitated towards the garden. But the bright sunshine was too much for their eyes, and they staggered back inside the patio. One child didn't feel well. A nurse took it to the sleeping area, where twenty sleeping bags and low pillows were laid out. Soon, all the children had been given a drink and a light meal, and were fast asleep. They had made the transition successfully.

But the beaming-down was not over. Large bags made of cushioned material were brought out and placed in a reception area. Glass bottles about a foot high began appearing. They fell into designated pockets inside the bags. Mexican staff lifted the bottles out and laid them on a long table for checking. The bottles contained thick grey and charcoal biscuits, the two colours arranged in a Yin-Yang pattern.

In fact, the biscuits were metallic rare earths, not commonly found on our planet. They would command a high price when sold for industrial processes. They came mainly from Planet Arturus, where mining plays a major part in their economy.

In the days that followed, adoption papers were prepared for all the children, and they were placed with well-to-do families in the United States, who worked for Sir Joseph's business contacts on Earth.

I asked to see what happened to earlier batches of children, and found myself in the classroom of a private school filled with teenage boys and girls. They wore uniforms and looked very studious. I remembered the words of the scientist on the mothership. 'Ours are ten to fifteen percent more intelligent than those of our competitors.'

"And what happens next?' I asked.

The scene changed to an Ivy League university. Smartly dressed young men and women holding books and papers were making their way into a building to attend a lecture. These children were certainly not deprived in any sense. They had a full parental upbringing and the best start in life. Funds from the sale of the rare earths, beamed-down in the glass bottles, covered all their costs.

'So, who's behind all this?' I asked.

Next moment, we were back in the office of the chief executive, Sir Joseph, who had met his end so suddenly. He and his deputy had been replaced by two other brown tweed-suited members of the Board. The new chief was discussing progress on their Earth export business.

'It's been going on for over forty years. Our original child batches did not do as well as expected, mainly because the level of intelligence of our subjects was not sufficiently above average, and few of them made it any higher than US State level. These days our subjects have greatly enhanced intelligence, and we focus on placing them in professional careers — legal, banking and business, before entering politics, first at state level and then nationally. We also need to place our people on think-tanks and lobby groups. In the current climate, our gender base is broadly fifty/fifty males and females.'

'I understand we are getting better results now,' said his new deputy.

He was less familiar with this side of the work than his boss, having specialised in mining.

'Yes,' said the chief, 'there is no doubt that the more recent genetic modifications and upgrades have had a beneficial impact. Our placements now have the best minds in the business, and when we can interest them sufficiently, they are developing the kind of career portfolios that make for a good political background.

Our objective is to control the direction of politics at the highest levels, primarily in the United States and United Nations, as well as other parts of the world, to ensure that Earth's legal frameworks favour our commercial interests, particularly on mining and environmental issues. Ultimately, we want to control the way that disclosure of interplanetary space programmes is conducted, to ensure that when it happens, our interests are represented in the best light.'

'How exactly do you go about interesting someone in specific professions, let alone a career in politics?' asked the deputy.

The chief smiled and reached across his desk. He pressed a switch and a plasma screen came down from the ceiling.

'Watch this,' he said, selecting a video from a bank of

options displayed on the top of his desk. As we watched, the screen showed a dedicated space station close to Earth. In every room, technicians were operating listening devices, WiFi surveillance technologies and Functional

Magnetic Resonance Imaging screens.

'Our children have built-in microchip receptors in their heads, which we can track. Through their life, while they sleep, we transmit suggestions, dreams and images to steer them along specific paths,' explained the chief.

The scene inside the space station changed. White-coated men and women psychologists were holding discussions in meeting rooms about the progress of each child, and any adjustments needed to their education. They switched on plasma screen equipment and dialled up their collaborators on Earth, who had access to parents and teachers. Any difficulties in a child's development would be discussed, or if a child showed particular gifts, ways of supporting and enhancing those gifts would be explored.

'I wish I had been given such opportunities,' the deputy said, visibly impressed.

'Oh, there's no doubt about it, these are very special children, and they are becoming very special people,' said the chief. 'But if you are preparing men and women to represent our interests at the highest world levels, including the President of the United States, the investment is worth it.'

'Do they know what is happening to them?' asked the deputy.

'They have no idea whatsoever,' replied the chief. 'They do not have any recollection of their time off-planet, and it is up to the foster parents what they are told about their early childhood.'

'Then you couldn't tell them apart from anyone else,' said the deputy.

His voice lowered to a whisper, as he considered the impressiveness of the operation unfolding before him.

'No,' said the chief, 'apart from one thing. Ours are just in a different class when it comes to intelligence and capability.'

At that moment, the chief's executive secretary, came in.

'The environmental delegation has arrived, Sir,' she announced.

'We'd better go,' said the chief, switching off the plasma screen.

He and his deputy moved into an adjoining room where thirty well-heeled men and women were being offered drinks and nibbles. Other members of the Board joined them and mingled with the guests on the terrace, where they were able to admire the perfectly landscaped view. Before dinner, they would hear a talk about the conglomerate's mining activities on several planets. No mention was made of the terrible working conditions experienced by miners. Instead, the guests were shown action taken to protect mining sites from environmental damage during and after completion of mining. It was going to be another late night at the office.

I wanted to know what was in the products imported in bottles. The best person I could think to ask about that was a scientist called Lars, an astrophysicist from Norway who specialised in space geology, and who had worked on a European Space Agency project in the UK. I assisted him with a small part of his research in 2018/19. See *Kiss Terror Goodbye*. Recalling his frequency, I tuned into his image.

Lars was in a large, well-furnished office, linked to a

series of science laboratories. His office had dark-brown, wool sofas and executive chairs. Lars wasn't wearing a white lab coat. His hair seemed less grey and he looked younger and in better health. A smart lady with dark hair was sitting opposite him talking.

At first, I didn't recognise her, without her lab coat. It was Marion, the professor of biological sciences from London University, who had produced a joint report with Lars on investigations into planets with potential for human colonisation. It looked as if Lars and Marion had left the public sector and gone into business together.

Lars looked up and saw me.

'Oh, hello,' he said. 'Is there something you want?'

'Yes,' I replied, 'Please can you analyse this?'

I produced one of the grey-charcoal biscuits. 'What is that?' asked Lars.

'It's from off-planet mining,' I said.

'I don't have the equipment for that kind of analysis any more,' Lars said, looking rather disinterested.

'That's all right. I can make it for you,' I reassured him. 'Oh, all right,' said Lars, shrugging his shoulders.

I produced all the equipment and sliced off a small cross-section of biscuit for analysis in the spectroscopy machine. Lars switched on the machine, and asked me to go and sit on the sofa, while he examined it.

While I was sitting there, Marion came and sat next to me. She knew who I was, but had little experience of communicating with people in electromagnetic form. She obviously thought I wanted a job working for Lars again, and decided to give me a straight answer right away. She took out a piece of A4 paper and wrote:

'WE DO NOT NEED YOU.'

I took the paper and turned it over and wrote, 'BUT I NEED YOU.'

'It's all right,' said Lars. 'I'm doing her a favour.'

I could see he had analysed the substance. I went back and looked over his shoulder. 'How did you get this stuff?' asked Lars.

'It got beamed-down from off-planet, using technology described in my second book,' I said.

'Is this going in your books as well?' asked Lars.

'Yes,' I said, 'Is there more than one substance in the sample I gave you?'

'There are two,' said Lars.

'Do they have military or industrial applications?' I continued.

'Both,' said Lars. 'One substance is not found on Earth. The other is, but it's very expensive. I cannot tell you what it is — not if it's going in your book.'

I guessed the information must be classified for government purposes, so I did not pursue the matter at that time. *9.

'That's all right,' I replied. 'I don't need to know more than general stuff.'

'Do the military know about this?' asked Lars.

'I should think so,' I said. 'They seem to keep a watching brief.'

'Why is it brought in? And where does it go?' Lars asked.

'A large conglomerate off-planet, with associated links on-planet, are importing it, and supplying it to their own business partners,' I said.

I produce a bottle of the biscuits a foot high, and put it on

Lars's desk

'Very interesting,' said Lars.

It looked as if I would not get any more information from him, so I decided to go. 'Do you want me to remove the kit I just produced?' I asked.

'No, leave it. We can use it,' Lars said.

'OK, thanks,' I said, and I left.

As I left, I heard Lars telling Marion, 'I couldn't say what it was, while she was here.'

'Why?' asked Marion. 'Is it uranium, or nuclear stuff?'

'No,' said Lars.

He picked up the bottle and looked at it.

'This should keep us going for some time,' he said.

Not long afterwards, I sensed that Lars wished to talk to me, and I returned to his office. Lars and Marion were standing there waiting for me.

'Ah, Martha,' said Lars. 'That jar you left here, could you make ten thousand more of them, please.'

'Why ask me?' I thought, 'Can't you make them yourself'?'

Then I remembered that he knew nothing about going Green, or creating things from mind. To help him get there quickly I said, 'Would you like me to give you both a frequency upgrade?'

Lars and Marion both said, 'Yes.'

I sent them both the Green energy. As they appreciated the meaning of what had happened to them, Lars and Marion turned to each other and held hands, looking into each other's eyes. So, they were not just business partners.

I asked Lars where he wanted the ten thousand bottles, and he suggested an empty warehouse he owned. I created them in large packing cases, and showed Lars a photo of them in the warehouse. Lars asked if the bottles could be redesigned to his specifications and have his business logo on them. So I fixed that. Finally, Lars asked me to produce all the business and government documentation to go with the "consignment", to make sure he could account for owning them, and having the right to use them.

I reminded the happy couple that they could now create anything they wanted for themselves. That way, if they wanted another warehouse full of the stuff, they knew what to do.

'You should have a go, to get used to doing it,' I said.

Lars decided to make a ball out of recycled paper. It appeared on one of his chairs. It was low tech, but at least he had got the idea.

Lars and Marion were smiling and up-beat. They obviously thought they were in the money. I hoped it would work out OK for them, but I did wonder what would happen if they flooded the Earth market with esoteric products. It's a cutthroat life in the world of big business, and they would need help.

It soon became clear that they had got the kind of help they needed. That night, I looked in on the warehouse where the bottles were stored, piled high in packing cases. The top packing case was open, and a woman on a stepladder was inspecting the contents of one of the bottles.

The warehouse was inside a larger building, and I noticed two armed soldiers with rifles, guarding access to the warehouse. Marion was standing in the kitchen next door. She offered both the soldiers a coffee. Outside in the street, a large, unmarked black van, was parked. The soldiers went out to the van and handed their rifles to a man in the back of the van.

Two more soldiers, who had just come on duty for the night shift, made their way towards the warehouse. They sat down outside the double doors and made themselves comfortable. Lars had obviously informed the British military what had happened. From now on, his activities would receive full military support.

I went back to the warehouse the next day. Security staff dressed as removals men were lifting the boxes into a van. Neighbours asked the men what was happening. They had seen soldiers going into and out of the house the day before. The men said they knew nothing about that, and that the people who lived there were just moving house.

Now that Lars's business seemed to be getting off to a good start, I thought it was only fair to visit his former colleagues in the Surrey Space Centre, which is part of Surrey University, and offer them similar support. A group of them were working on technologies for space stations, when I appeared in their laboratory.

'Ah, Martha!' said one of them. 'We heard you did something to help Lars. Any chance of helping us?'

'That's just why I'm here,' I said.

'We need Beryllium,' said one white-coated man. 'Lots of it. Please can you put it in that glassed-off room over there. It's not safe to have the dust floating around in here.'

'Sure,' I said, and I filled the glassed-off room with dark grey ore.

It was nothing special to me, but the scientists were pleased. I looked Beryllium up in Wikipedia, and it said that 'Beryllium metal is used for lightweight, structural components in the defence and aerospace industries in high-speed aircraft, guided missiles, spacecraft and satellites.'

'Would you like to be able to make whatever materials you need, using your mind?' I asked.

'Look, Martha, we already know about going Green,' said another scientist impatiently. 'We just need you to do it, please.'

'OK,' I said, and I sent Green energy to all of them.

All the scientists looked very relieved. They started making the raw materials they wanted for their work, and I left them to get on with it. With Britain leaving the EU and going it alone, they needed all the help they could get.

THE BIG PLAN UNCOVERED

Next day, I came under attack from large numbers of terrorists in my house. They were mainly from Mexico and Asia, though their leaders were still from the States. A terrorist supervisor leaned forward, pointing his weapon at me.

'I'll get the little nastiness out of here, fast!' he muttered.

I created a command 'DEAD' which immediately killed all the murderers and sent their bodies to the location on the Mexican border where the US military were monitoring activities. I arranged for all victims and junior terrorist ranks, who had been forced into the war against their will, to receive Green energy. Doing that released them from the electromagnetic environment forever.

In the following week I was attacked continually with such renewed intensity that I began to wonder if it had something to do with the ten thousand bottles of mineral products which I created for Lars. It could have flooded a rather specialist market, and if so, who stood to lose? It had to be the conglomerate based on planet Arturus. I created a new command:

"All people in the universe involved in attacks on the Free World, DEAD."

Then I went to the Mexican border, to check on things. A large number of dead men were piling up all over the place.

'What's happening?' I asked the US guards.

'We've got men from all over space coming in,' a guard replied. 'Looks like about ten thousand of them.' The US guards were used to dealing with large numbers of terrorists, which they intercepted in huge nets suspended above ground. I took a look, and amongst the piles of bodies, I recognised the tweed suits worn by senior members of the conglomerate from Planet Arturus. I switched my attention to the room of the chief executive on that planet. The head man was standing in his office talking to two soldiers.

'My deputy was here a moment ago. Then he dropped dead on the floor, and his body disappeared,' he said.

'Right,' I thought, 'that means that the deputy was actively participating in attacks against the Free World, and got picked up by my programme.'

I went back to the US guards on the Mexican border, and explained the situation. 'Shall I bring the chief executive in for questioning?' I asked.

'Wait,' said one of the guards. 'If this is coming from another planet, it's not for us to deal with. There are higher ranking people above us who need to be consulted. I'll go and talk to them.'

The guard went into a building on the US side of the border. After a few minutes he returned. 'Bring him in here,' he said. 'We'll take him upstairs.'

I went to planet Arturus, to the chief executive's office, selected the chief, and transported him to the ground outside the US building. The man was understandably shocked.

'What is the meaning of this?' he shouted. 'Where am I? Put me back immediately.' Two guards took him by each arm.

'You're coming with us, Sir,' they said, and led him inside.

I followed them into an interrogation room several floors

above. Two US border control officials were waiting. I explained that the man was the chief executive of a huge conglomerate from another planet, and suspected of masterminding hostile activities against the Free World. They contacted another branch of the US military, and the man was taken into a secure room in the building, where three men were waiting to question him.

'I am completely innocent,' said the chief. 'I know nothing about these activities. If my deputy was involved at any level, he never let me in on it.'

'That is not true,' I said, 'and I can prove it. He's got a video on his desk which shows how a space station just outside the Earth's atmosphere is monitoring and influencing people planted on Earth, to subvert political processes in the US.'

'Is that true?' asked one of the interrogators.

'Of course not!' said the chief.

'I can bring in the desk, if it's OK with you,' I said.

'Sure, go ahead,' said the interrogator.

I selected the chief's desk and took a copy of it. Then I pasted the desk into the interrogation room, adjusting it to fit. A plasma screen unfolded on the wall, and began to play the video that showed the activities on the illegal space station targeting Earth. The men watched, as it covered the activities of the mind control technicians and the psychologists in charge of the human subjects being influenced in the US. The chief Executive knew the game was up. He tried to use the command that rescued terrorists who wanted out of the war.

'I want to go to the United States!' he shouted, hoping to claim asylum at the US military's New York portal.

There was a silence. Nothing happened, because he was in the home of the US military, and their high-level security blocked absolutely everything. He had obviously been watching how I used these commands to rescue people, but it wouldn't help him here. The chief executive looked round helplessly, starting to panic. Military men, who had been monitoring the interrogation process from another room, came in.

'OK, you can take him away,' they said, and the chief executive was led out. One of them turned to me.

'Are you sure the enemy space station is close to Earth?' he asked, 'Our technicians can't locate it.'

"Maybe it is using stealth technologies,' I suggested.

'Can you put a tracking marker on the inside of the station?' another man asked.

'Give me a minute,' I replied, and I sent myself over there.

Making myself invisible, I went inside, and put a thick marker on the ceiling of one of the operations rooms. Then I heard a shout from the US military building. 'Yes, we've got it. My God! Look where it is! Just look at that!'

I returned to the building. The men were now in another room full of technicians operating observation equipment.

'OK, thank you, we'll take it from here,' said one of the military men, dismissing me with a wave of the hand.

There were men crowding round the viewing screens. Other men were getting themselves organised to operate equipment at the far end of the room, and I could see another group of men putting on space suits. There was nothing more I could do to assist so I left. But soon afterwards, I returned to the enemy space station, invisibly, to see what was going on. Two US military space vehicles were positioned on either side of the space station, and men were attaching towing gear around it.

Other US military men were on the top of the space station, operating infra-red equipment. One of the enemy technicians from the alien space station, who had volunteered to help the US military, was up there with them.

'What's the name of your planet anyway?' asked a US military astronaut.

'We call it Arturus, after the legend of King Arthur,' replied the technician. 'The name is very popular in human planets around this galaxy.'

'I see, so you're all knights of the round table, then?' laughed the US astronaut.

'You can laugh,' said the technician. 'But to us, it is an inspiring story of achievement in spite of overwhelming odds.'

'Hmm,' I thought to myself, 'Robin Hood would have been more appropriate, as he was an outlaw and a robber...'

I went inside the space station to see what was going on. No one was there. It was completely empty.

'I thought you said everyone was off the station,' a man shouted.

'I did,' his colleague replied.

'I just saw something in there. Can you run another check?' the man said. Quickly I removed myself.

'No, it's OK,' his colleague replied. 'Check negative, there's no one in there.'

'Right, let's go,' said the man, and they began to pack up their equipment, before towing the station into US military custody.

It was time to get out of the way, and I left the men to get on with it. But something was bothering me.

'How come the US military didn't spot a large space station just outside Earth's atmosphere?' I thought, 'You can't just overlook that.'

Tuning into the universe, I asked to meet whoever could answer my question. Next moment, I was on a different planet far away, looking down a hill full of topiary and formal gardens. Chinese-style pagodas blended into the landscape. I noticed a lot of surveillance cameras on trees in all directions.

At the top of the hill, was a large office building made from brown, reinforced glass. There were even more cameras around the entrance. I went in invisibly, and tuned in to find the right room. It was a modern workshop, with an upper level, surrounded by wooden railings that looked down onto the ground floor. There was a sign over the top of the doorway saying 'Apolonius.'

A man in his mid-forties, with pale skin and dark hair, wearing work overalls, was sitting at a table. He wore protective eye gear, and was constructing a piece of electronic equipment. I appeared in front of his table and he looked up.

'Hello,' I said.

'Ah,' said the man, 'I know who you are. You were out there looking at our cameras in the garden, weren't you?'

'Yes,' I said. 'I hope it's all right. I've come from Earth to ask you about shielding technologies.'

'Oh, yes,' said the man, 'I was expecting you.'

'Is your name Apolonius?' I asked.

'No,' the man laughed, 'that's the name of my firm. My name is Bertarus, but you can call me Berta.'

'How do you know about me?' I asked. Berta looked at me.

'Our planet, which is called Dipartu, was colonised by the US at the same time as many others were across the galaxy. We get our light from our local sun, from which we draw our energy. Shortly after we began to live here, we noticed that our intellectual development was advancing faster than that of people on other planets. We discovered that our sun emits radiation and particles which make us smarter.'

Berta lowered his voice.

'Smarter does not necessarily mean better. Don't get the idea that we are higher up the scale than others. In fact, we have gone backwards politically, and we are not a democracy now. But we have a lot of advanced technologies, which we use to tell us what is going on all over the galaxy. So that is how I know about you. I can read your thoughts, and I know why you are here.'

'Can you explain about the technology used to shield the hostile space station outside Earth?' I asked.

Berta nodded.

'Sure. It's one of our products. It's a superior coating which cannot be detected using conventional technologies. But don't worry, the US military have already been in touch with us this morning about it, and we are in the process of agreeing a protocol which will mean that we do not sell the product outside our planet.'

'I can see that Earth has a lot of catching up to do,' I said. 'Your planet is not the only one,' said Berta.

Then he added, 'Before you go, you might be able to do us a favour, if you have no objection.'

I guessed his meaning. He wanted Dipartu to go Green.

'Just give me a moment,' I said, and I selected the planet at subatomic particle level, and wished it to go Green.

Berta fell backwards in his chair, and a smile of appreciation came over his face. 'It's just like we'd been told,' he said. 'Thank you, Martha.'

'No problem,' I called back, as I left.

ORION WAR MOVIE

So far, I had visited planets colonised by people from the United States or, earlier, from the British Isles, from the 1920s to the 1960s. But there must have been humans in space who weren't from Earth originally. I decided to explore the Orion constellation, because it appears in human myths and legends, and might be a place to find people who hadn't come from Earth.

As I approached the vast area covered by the Orion constellation, it looked as if a tremendous electrical storm was going on. There were great flashes of light, and thunderous explosions, accompanied by orange-red clouds of smoke and fire. Scout ships were shooting out of the clouds in all directions. It was as if someone had just stepped on a wasp's nest.

'There must be a war going on,' I thought. An angel appeared.

'Don't go there, it's not safe,' said the angel. 'Can I just watch for a while?' I asked.

'Be very careful not to intervene,' said the angel, 'Provided you make sure that you can't be seen, you can go ahead.'

I switched to invisibility mode. 'What is the war about?' I thought.

As I watched, a black space vehicle drew up next to a

larger space transporter, which had the doors to its hold open. Caucasian men in black uniforms, wearing what looked like white motorbike helmets with a red stripe, stood at the doors. They belonged to an interplanetary Freedom Group, who were trying to fend off the attacks of another interplanetary group who called themselves 'Orion Alliance.' Men from the black space vehicle threw three captured enemies in shiny black armour and black helmets out of the space vehicle and into the cargo hold.

'Mercy! Mercy!' cried one of the enemies from the Orion Alliance, as he lay on the ground.

'We'll leave them here to die,' said a white-helmeted man, whose name was Tendel.

The men from the Freedom Group closed the hold doors, and went out. Once outside, they extracted the air from the hold, and the three enemies suffocated. After they were dead, the Freedom Group men returned and removed the helmets of the dead men. Two of the dead had

Caucasian features, dark hair and dark blue-black skin. The third man was a Caucasian with white skin and mid-brown hair.

'We've got two from the Alliance, and the third is one of ours,' announced a man called Haspar.

'One of ours?' asked Tendel.

'Yes,' said Haspar, 'they've been using him to pick our brains, as they cannot attune to our mind frequencies by themselves.'

'So, now they can read our minds!' said Tendel, who was becoming demoralised by long hours on the battlefield. 'There is no point in staying here. We'll have to go back to our planet. They have the advantage in fleet size, and they are using our minds against us.'

'We can't walk out on our colleagues,' said Haspar.

'We are no use to them here, we must get out of the area and start again,' replied Tendel. He took off his helmet despairingly.

'We can't win against them. Its hopeless,' he muttered as he walked along the corridor of the space transporter.

Tendel and Haspar turned a corner and walked out of sight. 'But what is the war about?' I repeated.

'Take a look and see,' said the angel.

I went down a black tunnel and into the hold of an Orion Alliance Group ship. As I emerged into the light above, there were rows of men with blue-black skin sitting at desks, their helmets next to them, completing work sheets. A man wearing a helmet came in and they handed their sheets to him.

'OK, you can go off duty now,' said the man.

The Alliance Group ship I had visited was docked underneath an enormous space city, full of soldiers, space craft and fighter ships. I wanted to see the people at the top, who were running this show. I found myself in a large room with a semi-circular table on a stage at one end. Behind the table, was a large wall display showing the Orion constellation, the positions of all the planets, and where fighting was going on. Planets owned by the Orion Alliance were shown in black and silver, the Alliance colours. Battle areas were shown in red. Planets not yet conquered were shown in grey.

The Alliance's strategy was to target a vulnerable planet which had weak defences, take it over and strip all its resources, both men and materials, to fund the takeover of the next planet. The result was a trail of desolation across the galaxy. The Alliance did not reap the benefit of its conquests, because it had trashed all the planets. All it could do was continue on from one planet to the next, and although it was winning, marginally, it was losing most of its men in the process.

A man in black uniform, with a black and white motorbike style helmet, whose name was Olvar, was sitting at the top table with two other men in black uniforms. All three men had Caucasian features, dark eyes and blue-black skin.

'We have to finish our task,' said Olvar. 'The Freedom Group will not surrender. They are fighting to the death.'

'We cannot go ahead without further support,' said Vangar, Olvar's deputy.

'We have no further support,' said Olvar

'Then we have to fight to the last,' said Vangar.

'Our main reason for fighting is to secure our goal. We have not obtained it. We must go on,' replied Olvar.

'We are not going to succeed without the loss of all our men,' argued Vangar.

'Then we will continue till the last one is dead. We cannot go back. We must go on,' Olvar insisted.

'I don't think we can,' said Vangar.

'If I have to fight to the last, I will fight on my own, until the war is won, and die if it comes to it,' said Olvar.

'There is another path,' said Vangar. 'We could do a deal with the other side, call for a ceasefire.'

'They would not trust us,' said Olvar. 'Besides, they are never reliable. We have to continue until we have taken over everyone in the galaxy. That is my goal, and that is what we will do.'

So there it was! I had the answer to my question. The war was about expanding territory and conquering everything in existence. Clearly, the Orion Alliance had a megalomaniac in charge, who was happy to sacrifice the lives of everyone in the galaxy for his criminally insane dreams of power. But it looked as if the result wasn't going to be a win for either side. Most of the Alliance's armies were manned by slaves from conquered planets. They were forced into it against their will, and most of them were getting killed.

I returned to the battlefield. It was like watching a 3-D movie. There were people dressed in armour, flying about in space, using personal space transporters. There was a huge flash like a supernova. It was so bright I had to shield my eyes. These people had powerful, explosive weapons.

There was a great deal of hardware floating around, and it was not always clear which side was driving it. There were large, oblong, space cargo-carriers. The hold of one cargo-carrier opened up, and ejected its cargo into space. The cargo was a fleet of used vehicles, including vintage cars like 1930s Bentleys.

What were these cars doing floating about in space? They came from a Freedom Group ship, and each car was packed with explosives which detonated on impact. They were being used as land-mines in space, recycled for the war effort. But they were just as likely to crash into a Freedom Group ship as an Alliance ship. The Freedom Group must have been desperate to resort to such measures.

There were huge rockets with pointed cones, which were guided remotely, and exploded when detonated. They belonged to the Orion Alliance. The Alliance also deployed long, black, fighter space craft. They looked like cigars with a back dorsal fin that rose at an angle of forty-five degrees. They could operate both on and off planet, and could drop bombs and fire missiles. The Freedom Group had black, fighter space craft which looked like US McDonnell Douglas F-15 Eagles. This was no coincidence, as most of the military hardware on the Freedom Group side had come from the US.

The space craft on both sides were powered by turbines which extracted electricity from gases originally from space plasma, and were linked to generators. There were electricity storage units, which ensured that space craft never ran out of fuel. Well, that is a rather basic description of a technology which we do not have on Earth, and which I do not pretend to understand in detail. Anyway, these things were flying about and worked efficiently.

But how could these space craft get into space without launchers? The Alliance Group had huge cargo bays suspended beneath their space city. The space craft were beamed-up there from the planets that produced them. All their resources were devoted to producing men and materials for the Alliance's galactic ambitions.

So was there an equivalent space city for the Freedom Group? Years ago, the US military assisted the Freedom Group, and built a series of large space stations in space, where men and materials could be beamed-up for defensive purposes. The space stations were still intact and operating well, because they were built in a high frequency band which the Alliance Group could not reach.

Sadly, the Freedom Group space stations were almost deserted, because there had been so many disastrous losses over the years since the war started. The technology came from the US, but the personnel came from the Freedom Group, who were relatively unskilled. They were defensive forces from local planets, which had been colonised earlier by the British and Americans. Some were trained military staff, some were volunteers, and some were conscripts.

An oblong, space cargo-carrier owned by the Orion Alliance appeared. The cockpit had side windows, and as I watched, one of the helmeted pilots wound down the window and leaned out, holding a rocket guidance system. The pilot guided a rocket to its destination, a cargo carrier owned by the Freedom Group. The rocket hit the carrier, piercing a hole in its side. Then it detonated, splitting the carrier in two. The pilots escaped using personal space transporters.

'How could the Alliance pilot wind down a window in a space craft?' I thought.

Suddenly it became clear. None of the space craft used by either side had pressurised cabins! They relied on helmets, which extracted gases from outside, filtered them, and provided additives which made breathable air.

Behind the front line, a large group of men using personal space transporters were building a secure electronic wall, to protect the Freedom Group armies. It drew power indirectly from space plasma, and was the Freedom Group's main advantage in the war. So far, the Alliance Group forces had not managed to penetrate it. The men building the wall were guarded by US-built fighter planes while they worked. The fighter planes could operate both on and off-planet.

A small Freedom Group spaceship flew by, on the wrong side of the wall, having just brought up a group of men to work on the construction process. The pilot, whose name was Aram, was wearing a space helmet, and talking to his boss on a communications device.

'Are you free to take on another assignment?' asked his boss.

'I've just delivered two hundred men out there. What more can I do in the time allocated?' Aram responded. Aram was a conscript, and his work schedule was measured in hours per day.

'OK, turn out of the area,' his boss replied.

Aram took a look round. The situation had changed rapidly for the worse in the last few minutes, as Orion Alliance reinforcements flew into the area.

'Not possible,' said Aram. 'There's too much enemy material flying about. Are there any fighter escorts available? I don't think I can leave the area without support.'

A huge rocket hit the cockpit windows, and went straight through Aram's ship without exploding. It was aiming at another spaceship, and had not been detonated. Aram crouched down, and two men in space suits, whose names were Mardet and Bordur came running over and got him out of the cabin.

'We must leave. Come on,' said Bordur.

The two men helped Aram into a scout ship, and they took off, through the explosions. 'Where? Where to?' cried Mardet, who was now piloting.

Bordur stood beside him at the controls.

'Turn away from the fighting,' he said, repeating the advice given to Aram.

The scout ship turned sharply away and fell into a downward path, out of the battle area. It coasted for a while, flying over friendly cargo-ships loaded with space vehicles, until the smoke cleared. The light from a sun showed the way to a planet. The scout headed down towards the planet but was barred from entry by a wall of electronic barriers.

What are we to do?' asked Mardet.

'We'll have to turn back,' said Bordur. 'Here let me drive.'

He took the controls and turned back, but looking upwards he saw a cargo-ship, directly above him. He dived down as fast as he could and just skimmed the electronic wall of the planet. As he did so, the scout's control panel blew, and the ship stopped, stuck on the wall. A large black military space vehicle came up fast towards them. Two armed guards with space helmets stood at the open cargo bay of the vehicle. The guards threw harnesses attached to cables to the three men.

'Come aboard,' they ordered.

Soon the three men were being escorted up into the space vehicle. They were marched down a corridor into a small room, where they were locked in.

'Now what?' said Mardet.

'Well at least we're alive,' said Aram.

'Yes, but for how long?' asked Bordur.

Five minutes later they were in front of a military commander.

'You have breached our defence system,' said the commander. 'The penalty for that is death — for an alien — but as you are not aliens, we'll have to let you in.'

The three men breathed a sigh of relief. 'You can go now,' said the commander. Turning to two soldiers, he ordered, 'Take them to their quarters. They can join the crew until we land.'

Next day, the space vehicle landed in a military area, and soldiers streamed out of exit points around the ship. Aram, Mardet and Bordur were taken to a small aircraft. It was oblong, with a long, thin, turquoise nose containing the engine. The top of the aircraft was transparent, and lifted up on both sides, to allow access to six seats, including those for the pilot and co-pilot. The three men sat at the back, and watched from the windows as the aircraft took off.

The aircraft landed on an airstrip in an area surrounded by forests. The men got out and shook hands with the pilots. They walked towards a low-level building at the end of the airstrip, and went inside. The building was manned by two military staff.

'We are from Bardon. We need to get home,' said Aram. 'Can you arrange that?'

'Yes, we know where you're from,' said one of the military staff. 'Everyone has heard about your great piloting skills. You will soon be back in your own base.'

That night, the three heroes were back where they came from. I caught up with them as they were sitting at a table in their canteen, drinking the traditional brown liquid that seemed to be available on most planets in the universe. A senior man in military uniform came over and sat with them.

'Your hearing will be tomorrow,' he said. 'Don't worry, it won't be too bad, it's good to have some of our men come back alive. Others were not so lucky.'

'How long must the war go on?' sighed Mardet.

I was wondering the same thing, when an angel appeared.

'The war will continue for many years,' said the angel. 'You cannot expect to sit and watch for ever. And it is not safe here.'

'So, Orion is closed for now,' I thought, 'but I want to know what happens in the end.'

As the question formed in my mind, I found myself fast-forwarded to a scene of devastation, with cities razed to the ground. What was left of the buildings was covered in grey ash. Several men from the Freedom Group, handcuffed to each other, were walking in a field. They wore metallic robotic suits, which needed to be powered-up. The men were ordered to lie down in rows, and their suits were connected to a power source. It was a prison camp, and as the men were weak, their slave-masters relied on robotics to give them the power needed for their work.

I felt cheated of a happy ending, believing that I had seen the last of the Freedom Group. But the faces of the three men, Aram, Mardet and Bordur, still haunted me.

'Maybe I don't want to know what happens in the end,' I thought…

SAMURAI AND THOR PEOPLES

I changed direction and moved far away into a quieter part of the Orion constellation. Then I saw a fleet of dark grey space ships, shaped like super-tankers. Invisibly, I boarded one of the ships, which had the name 'The Arturus,' written on its side.

'Honestly! That is so lacking in imagination!' I thought. 'Just about everything in space seems to be called "Arturus". But it tells you who's been manufacturing these ships. Planet Arturus probably makes them for the export market.'

I went below the top deck. The interior was dark grey, lacking the comforts of a modern aircraft. On one side of the ship, next to the outer wall, there were rows of tables, with two chairs behind each table. Caucasian children aged nine years old were sitting quietly at the tables, working with exercise books. Each child was tethered by the ankle to one of the table legs. That didn't look right to me.

Then I heard a loud 'crack.' A huge figure dressed like a Samurai warrior, completely covered in red and black satin, lined with gold brocade, and wearing a red and black helmet, was marching up and down, cracking a red and black whip, shouting, 'Keep up the work now!'

That didn't look right to me either. But the children appeared unconcerned. Wishing to help the children, I willed their shackles to disappear. The gang-master let out a shriek and ran off. The children smiled and turned round to talk to

193

each other, but they stayed sitting at their tables.

I moved up a level. Two tall people, dressed like Japanese geishas in pink and ivory silk, with tall, black headdresses and very white skin, came hurrying down the stairs. They seemed to be very concerned about wearing the right outfits.

'We'll have to change. They gave us no warning. Now here we are, looking like this,' said one of the "geishas" in a worried tone.

They had been sent to supervise the kids at short notice, and needed to get into their Samurai costumes. The clothes they were wearing didn't look quite right for geishas, so I went on the internet and checked on ancient Japanese imperial costumes. It was easy to find these clothes. They were Japanese Imperial Court dress from the mid-19th century. But contrary to what I had thought, the gear was for men, not women.

I now know that what I had seen was two men in imperial Japanese court dress, wearing men's kimonos. What looked like tall hairdos were in fact unusual black hats that fitted over the top of the head, and had a vertical construction on top. So they weren't meant to be geishas. They were courtiers.

I continued exploring the ship and went up a level. This level was designed for food preparation. Cooking equipment was lined up against one side of the ship on shelves. There were no chairs, but three men in kimonos were standing in a row, using a shelf as a table. Each one held a large fork in one hand.

'I'm not going down there,' said one of them.

'No,' said another. 'It's not safe.'

'Until they find out what's going on, I'm not taking a step down there,' said the third.

All three plunged their forks into large, oval pieces of fried bread about a foot long, and start munching.

'They sent us down here,' said the first courtier.

'And what have they done about it?' said the second courtier, raising his voice. I could hear voices on the floor above.

'Less noise down there!' shouted a voice.

I went upstairs to the top deck. This was where the ship's pilots worked. Two gang-masters in red and black samurai uniforms were standing up there, looking anxious. Towering over them, and clearly in charge, was a man with huge chest and arm muscles. He was seven feet tall, with very fair hair, and he looked just like our idea of the god Thor.

'I didn't put them down there,' he said. 'If they want their children brought here, they ought to make proper arrangements.'

He stared impassively into the ship's guidance system, as he managed the ship's controls. I decided to rescue all the children on the ship and send them to the US military electromagnetic border control in New York.

'Total population of children on all ships in the fleet, go the United States,' I announced.

The children were whisked away to the US ghouls border control portal. Seeing that they were children, the US portal officers let them in. The children laughed and played about as they were escorted into the secure compound. It was an adventure for them. I knew that the US military would repatriate them to their planet of origin.

'Where are they from?' asked the duty officer.

'I don't know,' I admitted. 'I found them on ships in space, shackled to tables.'

'Can you bring in their captors?' asked the duty officer.

'I'll do my best,' I said.

I went back to the ship's top deck. Several huge muscular men wearing black Samurai uniforms were standing there. They seemed to be security guards. One of them took off his helmet. He was another Thor type, but had light brown hair.

'The children have all gone, and we know whose fault that was, don't we?' he said, looking at one of the gang-masters.

'I didn't do anything,' said the gang-master. 'It was a "her". I distinctly heard a "her" say "total population of children" before they disappeared...'

'It can't have been a "her", said the pilot.

'Yes, it was. It was one of the fair sex,' insisted the gang-master.

'Well, you were the one who just said "they", so I'm arresting you.' said the Samurai security guard, illogically.

'Oh, I see, so I'm to be arrested for saying the word 'they' am I?' The gang-master's voice rose an octave higher with indignation.

'Well, oh, all right,' sighed the security guard, scratching his head, 'but someone must have done something...'

At that moment I said, 'Total population on this ship go to the US ghouls' portal,' and they all went straight there. 'Here they are,' I said to the duty officer.

'OK, we'll take them in for questioning,' he replied, and he escorted the colourful crew into the military area.

As I left, a thought crossed my mind.

'It's just like the movie "Flash Gordon!" Makes you wonder whether the author of the cartoons knew something.'

The ship's crew seemed to be from a mix of different cultures, like sailors on commercial cargo ships. I wanted to find out more about them, but at that moment, I was interrupted by a concerted terrorist attack from Earth. The terrorists had stronger fire-power than usual and wore shielding which made them look as if they were wearing rubber car tyres under their clothing.

The attack felt different from usual, and lacked direction, as if the attackers were unfamiliar with their environment or the purpose of their war. I pulled one of the attackers out of the throng, and willed his armour to come off. As the armour came off, I recognised the men as being the same kind as had shot the chief executive of the conglomerate on Arturus. They were space pirates! But what were they doing on Earth, attacking me? I selected them all and sent them to the US military.

Next thing, a lot of huge men with big muscles, wearing helmets and Roman-style armour appeared. They were the same as the Thor look-alike I had seen on the space ship.

'This is getting too much,' I thought. 'Why should I have to put up with alien terrorist invasions. That is a matter for the military.'

But these guys couldn't just appear at my address out of nowhere. They had to arrive via an electromagnetic medium, and someone on Earth had to help them. They were clearly working with the US terrorists, and must have been on Earth before they attacked me. I decided to reverse-engineer their arrival mechanism, to see where they had got in.

With a whoosh, the whole lot went back to the place where they had been input to the US terrorist computer system in miniature form. I recognised it. It was on the Mexican side of the US-Mexican border, just behind a US electromagnetic military portal in New Mexico.

'It would be good to make all the bad guys full size, so

that the US and Mexican military realise that they have an alien problem,' I thought.

So I said, 'Select all alien terrorists. All alien terrorists go full size, real world outside.'

This had the effect of turning them back into their normal size, in our world. But I had overlooked one thing. When you send Earth ghouls 'full size, real world outside,' they are left wearing long, white shifts. But the aliens had not been given any underwear. So when I gave the command to go full size, real world outside, they shot up into the real world, completely naked.

The unclothed aliens found themselves standing in the centre of a traffic roundabout, in a busy Mexican market place, shouting threats at the passers-by. An interested group of Mexican pedestrians soon gathered. They stared at the musclebound Thor types, with their rippling arms and chests, strong legs and large private parts. The Thors responded to this attention by shouting even more hostilities.

For a moment, the Mexicans stood there, their faces impassive. Then they all bent down, picked up stones from the ground, and started throwing them at the naked aliens. The stones bounced harmlessly off the bulging muscles of the Thor guys. The Thors began catching the stones as they arrived, and throwing them back. Suddenly, there was a whirring sound in the sky, as several military helicopters converged on the roundabout. Large nets came shooting out of the helicopters, which scooped up the aliens and took them away.

The Mexican military came to inspect the roundabout. They detected that there was an underground construction beneath it, which the terrorists had been using to input people to the ghouls' computer system, and down-size them. Clearly this was not the Mexicans' first contact with ghouls, as they started digging and pulling out miniature terrorists, like ants from an underground nest. More Mexican military men arrived, carrying black and pink mini pigs in their arms. The pigs looked like pet dogs, rather friendly and cuddly, but they were not pets.

'Our pigs are good little pigs,' said a Mexican, patting one of them.

The men placed the pigs on the ground and they started sniffing around. Then they caught the scent of the ghouls and their noses went down. Soon they were turning over the ground, snuffling out all the down-sized terrorists and crunching them up with obvious enjoyment. After a while, there were no terrorists left underneath the traffic island.

ELYANTHA, THOR PEOPLE AND SAMURAI

After the alien invasion, I set up a series of commands which ensured that all aliens entering the Earth's atmosphere automatically got diverted to the US military ghouls' border control portal. It looked as if the US Mafia and Islamic State terrorists had got a deal going with alien criminals, a kind of intergalactic unity guild. But who were these Thor types, and where had they come from? I launched myself into space and went in search of them. After a while, I arrived in a part of the universe that was completely new to me.

A small, glowing-green planet in the Draco constellation, called Orchia, caught my attention, and I descended through cloudy skies and mist onto the land below. I could see a garden city, with extensive grounds and open-air structures, surrounding tented pavilions. The country, which was called Elyantha, was full of oak woods. The trees had been cleared out of the city, except for a few near the pavilions.

I followed the lines of lawns and pavilions up to a hilly area, where there was a raised stage, made from earthworks, covered in grass. Rows of standards on poles flanked the sides of the stage and in the middle at the back were several thrones.

There were a lot of very tall, strongly-built, Thor-type men and women, standing around the earthworks, dressed in ancient looking clothes. The men wore long grey tunics and long trousers, with sandals. The women who were as tall as the men, with long fair hair tied in plaits, wore long blue and green fitted dresses, with square cut necks and long flowing scarfs.

Behind the stage, was a large palace, built of oak wood and roofed with oak beams. Instead of roof tiles, there were rows of waterproof leaves, which overhung the edge of the roof. I went into the palace, and looked around. There were long, oak tables, oak benches and high-backed chairs with carved arm supports at each end. A very tall woman in a grey-green dress walked towards me. Her name was Lareth. I appeared before her. She stared at me with piercing, green eyes.

'Who are you?' she asked, 'and how did you get in here?'

'My name is Martha, and I am from planet Earth,' I said, 'I have come because men from your planet have been attacking me.'

'Sit down,' said Lareth, pointing to a smaller table, with two carved chairs facing each other. 'Our people are not war-like,' said Lareth.

'Are you a leader of your people?' I asked. Lareth bowed her head.

'Yes, I am a leader,' she said, 'and I rule with my brother Tyrell. You may have seen him standing out there, holding consultations with his men.'

'If you are not war-like, how is it that your men are attacking me?' I asked.

Lareth reached out her hand and touched my head, making a thought connection with me. 'Ah, I see!' she cried. 'These are space pirates!'

'We have no quarrel with Earth. In fact, we have trading arrangements with your planet, and long ago, our ancestors

201

visited your world. We are distant cousins from the past.'

'Are the space-pirates outside your control?' I asked. Lareth laughed and shook her head.

'It is not quite like that,' she said. 'They are criminals who have been banished from Elyantha. Come with me and I will show you.'

She walked towards a window. It had no glass in it, but as the temperature was pleasantly warm, there was no need for that. Lareth pointed towards the mountains in the distance.

'Look to the far horizon,' she said.

I looked along the line of her hand, over the woods and out to the farthest extent of the mountains. This would not be possible, on Earth, but Orchia's electromagnetic environment made it easier to send your mind out at a distance. At the edge of the mountains there was a portal manned by security guards. Electromagnetic ramparts fringed the entire area. Men and women were walking in and out through the portal in a peaceful manner.

'It is not possible for criminals to enter any of our lands, because they cannot get through the portals. So, if they are banished, they have to find a way of living elsewhere. Some of them get work on commercial space ships and do quite well. But others carry on their criminal activities. Those are the ones that become space pirates.'

'Where would people banished from your realm, learn how to pilot commercial space ships?' I asked.

'Our land is not the only one on this planet,' said Lareth, 'There is a large industrial city with modern buildings, a long way from here. That is where our planet carries out trade with other planets, and that is where people banished from our land go to earn a living.'

'But why would they come to Earth to attack me?' I asked.

Lareth paused for a minute, as if searching for the answer from the airwaves, then she said, 'You see, there are alliances of international criminals on our planet, and they are linked to off-planetary groups of criminals who work together and assist each other. You have criminals on your planet, and they also have links to off-planetary groups, and our criminals have been called on to assist yours.'

'Ah! Right!' I said. 'Now I understand. I guess I'll have to deal with that when I get back.' I was keen to go back to Earth and sort things out. I turned to Lareth, and bowed.

'Thank you for the information. Before I go, there is something I might be able to do to assist your people.'

'Oh, I know,' Lareth smiled. 'You mean going Green. Yes, we would like to have that.'

So I selected the planet at subatomic level, and turned it Green. Up to now, I felt there was a depressing atmosphere on Planet Orchia, probably too many oak trees. Suddenly, it was as if the sun had come out. Lareth went out onto the stage area, where her brother Tyrell was talking with his courtiers.

'Lareth, there you are, what has happened? Something has changed. Don't you feel it?' said Tyrell.

'Our planet has gone Green, at last,' said Lareth, smiling. She put her hand on Tyrell's shoulder.

'Come and meet my new friend, Martha.'

Tyrell came over and bowed his head toward me.

'We have heard stories about a visitor who brings gifts. You are most welcome here.' A tall, young man with light brown hair called Meron, joined Tyrrel. Tyrrel gave him a hug.

'This is Meron,' he said. 'Our lives are joined together. Now that our planet has upgraded, our work will be much easier. No more tree chopping for us after this.'

He gave me a look that said, 'Now we have the power, watch us play!' and turning towards a nearby hill, he said, 'Let our new home be over there.'

A large imposing wooden building with split level roofs appeared.

'Let's go and make the furniture,' said Meron, and the two men went off together. I looked at Lareth, a little surprised.

'How is rulership decided in your country,' I asked. 'Is it by family line?'

'Yes,' said Lareth. 'I know what you want to ask. Do I and my brother have any descendants, and if so, how were they created?'

'Well, I was just wondering…' I said.

Lareth took my arm and we walked under the oak trees.

'To us, Earth customs are very strange,' she said. 'We do not need a man and a woman to make a baby.'

'OK?' I said.

'On Orchia, women who have reached maturity give birth on their own, when they wish to do so. But we give birth to two possibilities, which you would call males and females. To us, that distinction is not so important. The males have physical strength beyond the females, for protection of our race in war, and for building our cities. But we share rulership between us.'

I started thinking about worker bees and soldier bees.

'I guess it could be like that,' I thought to myself. 'But even queen bees have to mate with males on Earth.'

'You have to widen your concepts, Martha,' said Lareth.

'I don't see any other women here,' I said. 'It would help me to understand, if I saw a few more of them, I think.'

'This way,' said Lareth, guiding me down a set of wooden steps.

We entered a clearing in the woods. There was a long, wooden table with solid chairs around it. Several tall, strong-looking women were siting chatting, and drinking from carved wooden cups.

'Do your people have close partner relationships?' I asked.

'Of course,' said Lareth. 'It's not always man to man or woman to woman, it can be both or either. You see that woman over there...'

Lareth pointed to a tall, mature woman who appeared to be organising a meeting with other men and women. The woman looked up as Lareth pointed towards her, and gave a nod, acknowledging her.

'We had a close relationship,' said Lareth, 'but that was long ago. We have grown and developed in our lives, and these days, we are involved in guiding our people. But our lives will always run in parallel. We do not lose what we had, but allow each other room to grow.'

'Do all these women have children?' I asked.

'They do,' said Lareth, 'and so do I, but our children have grown up now. These women are involved in decision-making for our city. You haven't seen our city, have you?'

She pointed towards a high bank. 'Go and look there.'

I climbed up the bank and looked down. Below me was a vast valley. Wooden houses in clearings stood out among the trees, and wide streets, made from wooden planks placed flat on the ground, extended the length and breadth of the city. Groups of children stood talking with their teachers and playing with hexagonal balls in wooden compounds nearby.

Men and women carrying

provisions walked along the streets, busy with daily duties. In one corner of the road, a group of men were using their new-found Green skills to produce textiles with abstract patterns on them, and adapting the textiles to make themselves tunics.

I turned back to the women seated round the table. They beckoned me over, and we talked for a while about how things were on our planets. It opened my eyes to many new possibilities, and I would have liked to talk longer, but I was conscious that time was going by and I needed to return home.

'Thank you for letting me see how you live,' I said. 'I will have to leave now, but I will not forget your peaceful way of life.'

Lareth clapped her hands and waved, as I faded out of their world.

Next day, I went back to the fleet of space ships that I met in the Orion constellation, and boarded 'The Arturus.' There were no children there now, but the ship had a new crew. The crew's hierarchy was the same — Thor-types piloting, Samurai and courtiers carrying out other duties. I went up to the top deck. The 'Thor type,' whose name was Mankar, was guiding the ship. A Samurai warrior, Nartur and two courtiers, Beytin and Goran, were sitting with him.

'It's not my fault I'm here,' said Beytin. 'I wish I could go home.'

'So do I,' said Goran.

Mankar sighed.

'I can never go home. They won't let me in. Only people who've gone Green are allowed back.' I appeared in front of the group, and there was a gasp.

'Why it's our Martha!' said Mankar, smiling.

The courtiers and the Samurai warrior gathered round me bowing humbly, and touching my hand. 'Please send me home,' they begged.

'We didn't volunteer to do overseas work,' said Beytin. 'Our bosses forced us into it.'

'Don't worry, I will help you all,' I said, 'But we mustn't forget those on the other ships in the fleet. Do all the ships have pilots from Elyantha?'

'Yes,' said Mankar.

'Right,' I said.

I sent Green energy to all the pilots and selecting them, I set them down outside the security fence at Elyantha. The men smiled and greeted each other, as they waited their turn to present themselves for checking and admission at the portal. All were let through without question, now that they had gone Green. They knew their way home, and were soon back with their families.

I turned to the courtiers and the Samurai warrior. 'Are you from Orion or Draco?' I asked.

'If you please, we are from Draco, and all from planet Ovolcha,' said Beytin.

'Yes,' said Nartur, 'my uniform is different from these two, but we are all the same, and come from the same city. We dress in different outfits depending on which work we are doing.'

'What is the purpose of the uniforms?' I asked.

'When we work on space ships, we have to represent our planet at intergalactic level, and our rulers want us to wear our national dress for that role,' explained Goran.

I selected all the courtiers and Samurai warriors in the

fleet, and sent them Green energy. While they were getting used to their new state of being, I went to planet Ovolcha and turned it Green at subatomic particle level. It had a low frequency, and I could tell there had been a lot of oppression there. When I got back, the little group were waiting for me. Already, they looked younger and less stressed.

'Are you going to send us all home now?' asked Goran. 'Yes, and I will come with you,' I said.

Selecting all the courtiers and warriors on the fleet of ships, I sent them all back to their home towns. Then I followed Beytin, Goran and Nartur, as they arrived back. Their village was made up of egg-shaped houses, with domed roofs, all built very close together, stacked against the side of a hill. There was a wide, white road, running down beside the houses. The little group stood there for a minute.

'It doesn't seem the same,' said Goran.

'No, it's definitely changed,' said Beytin.

'Changed for the better, I think,' said Nartur.

A man of Japanese appearance, with short dark hair, wearing a simple tunic, and trousers, came out of one of the houses nearby.

'Beytin! Beytin!' he cried.

Beytin ran over and hugged him. Then they turned and walked back into the house.

'I think I can see my home,' said Goran. A moment later he was gone.

Nartur and I walked down the hill. At the bottom, we came to a gate. Nartur turned to me. 'I have to go now — this is my place,' he said.

I waved the Samurai warrior goodbye.

ORION CELTIC PLANET

That was my last visit to the Constellation of Draco. My mind went back to Orion, and the three comrades — Aram, Mardet and Bordur,

'Did the Orion war involve all the planets?' I thought.

I tuned into the universal computer, and asked to go to a planet in the Orion group that was not at war. Then I saw a blue-green planet in the distance. Soon I was descending through a clear, bright atmosphere, looking down on green and brown lands, fringed with golden beaches and blue-green seas.

I arrived inside a city on a planet called Undaroch. The buildings were a mix of futuristic turrets and post-modernist, municipal smoked-glass. All buildings had security guards at the entrances, wearing helmets. I moved invisibly into a two-story building, which was full of children doing school studies at wooden desks, with a teacher at the front, writing on a black board. That suggested this culture had been in contact with Earth's Western civilisation in the past.

The children looked Celtic, with dark brown or red hair. They wore school uniforms similar to those worn by children in Europe and the States in the 1920s. A guard came into the school room and took off his helmet. He had the same features and colouring as the children. The guard announced in a kindly manner that it was time for lunch. He escorted the children downstairs into the basement where there was a canteen.

I went outside to look at the city, shining in the sun. It had been carefully planned on a series of hills, with important buildings on the tops of the hills, surrounded by trees. The narrower roads leading up the hill were not designed for cars, and I did not see any.

Below the city was a wide, sandy beach looking out onto a bay. As I looked up at the hills, a huge brown-yellow dragon, with scales, wings and a tail, flew by, holding an enormous, red fruit in its mouth. It looked spectacular, silhouetted against the sky above the hills. Out in the bay, a green sea-dragon, it's body a mass of coils, frolicked in the blue-green waves.

I went to the main legislature building. It did not have facilities for representation of the people, and was clearly not a democracy. A group of Celtic-looking men arrived wearing cloaks and helmets, with tunics and trousers in dark colours. They sat round a top table, and began discussing civic matters.

Their chairman, Andaros, was the leader of the council. He had grey hair and was older than the rest. On the wall was a striking picture of Andaros's wife, Erika, wearing a regal pearl circlet on her head. She was pale, with blue eyes, and had very long red hair cascading down her back in waves. The words underneath the picture described her as 'Chairwoman of the People's Parliament.'

Andaros called the group to order.

'My friends, it is sad news we have to share. I have been contacted by the head of the Draco planetary group. They no longer wish to be in contact with us, and are reviewing all their interplanetary relationships in the light of a recent upgrade. Our individual trading partners will be in contact shortly.'

'I have heard of these upgrades,' said a man sitting opposite Andaros, whose name was Petaroc. Petaroc leaned forward.

'They say that after the upgrades, people lack for nothing and do not suffer ill-health.'

'I've heard that too,' said another councillor, whose name was Levich. 'If this goes on, and we are left out, we will be at a disadvantage.'

'We must be cautious and alert to external threats,' said Andaros. 'We must monitor all our intergalactic contacts, so that we can anticipate changes in relationships with our trading partners as early as possible.'

At that moment, a messenger, clothed in grey metallic material which covered his head, brought a letter on a circular tray. The letter was enclosed in a square-shaped paper that had been folded and sealed. The messenger bowed and offered the letter to Andaros. He opened it, and stared at it in silence.

'This is not in our language,' he said.

He turned and spoke to a servant standing in attendance, 'Can you get an interpreter.'

The interpreter arrived, and bowed before the committee.

'What do you make of this?' asked Andaros, handing him the letter. The interpreter scanned the contents.

'It is in a Draconian language. Ah, yes, it states in the heading that it is from the head of Planet Utaroch. Following the recent upgrade to planet Orchia, they are suspending all intergalactic relations pending an internal review, and hope to be in contact in due course.'

Andaros sighed.

'Even our closest Draconian trading partners seem to be having second thoughts. Can you bring us a full written transcript as soon as possible?' he requested.

The interpreter bowed and left.

'What do you think it means?' asked Levich.

'Does it mean war?' asked Petaroc.

'No,' said Andaros, 'but we must get this upgrade. I wish I knew how.'

I left the room, and standing outside, selected planet Undaroch at subatomic level and sent it Green energy. When I returned, the councillors had got up from the table, looking as if a burden had lifted from their shoulders.

'I can sense something. There has been a change.' said Levich.

'I think it must be the upgrade,' said Petaroc, 'Nothing else could make us feel like this.'

'Let's go outside in the sun,' said Andaros.

The men went out onto the courtyard and stood above the wide, white steps leading down into the city. As they looked across the bay towards the horizon, something moved in the distance. Then there were several things moving. They came closer. It was a school of smallish whales, leaping over the waves and diving in the water. They came right into the bay and up towards the beach. Then they turned round and swam out again.

'They're back! They're back!' cried the men.

People came running out of the building towards the sea, and stood watching. 'It is a sign of better things,' said Andaros.

'How many years is it since the whales have been seen here?' asked Petaroc.

'Not since my great-grandfather's time,' said Levich.

The men laughed as the tension eased. Their intergalactic trading problems were over.

'I think we can reply to Planet Utaroch's letter,' said Andaros. 'We should also write to Orchia and the other Draco planetary heads. We can give them the good news. Undaroch has received the upgrade and is open for business.'

A group of women in long white and yellow satin dresses embroidered with small flowers and leaves came out of the council building and walked down the steps towards the sea. They represented a committee responsible for education and apprenticeships. Their leader, a woman with long, wavy, red hair, waved to Andaros as she passed. You could see the resemblance between the two.

'My daughter, Apella,' said Andaros, waving back, 'How busy we will all be. now that we have the upgrade. There is so much that needs to change. But at least we can make a start...'

I left them on the steps of the council building, with the sea glinting in the bay, and the raucous cries of dragons echoing from the mountain orchards in the distance.

Next day, I was granted an audience with Andaros's wife, Erika. She was a senior businesswoman, dressed in grey, who spent a lot of time in committees and working on papers at her desk. She explained that the People's Parliament was a consultative body of representatives, but they were not elected, and did not have voting powers.

'Our planet is ruled by a royal blood-line, and I am its Queen,' said Erika. 'My marriage was arranged when I was young. I have a son and daughter, and they both share in the duties of government.'

'I have seen your daughter and her committee members,' I replied.

'My son Arthur is working quite hard with me already. He is the elder of my two children,' Erika explained.

'We have our own contacts with Earth. Long ago our people visited your planet, including the lands now known as

Ireland, Iraq and Egypt. Egypt was their favourite place, because it had such a lush, tropical climate.'

'Our planet has enjoyed peace for a long time,' Erika continued. 'But now, no planets can feel secure. We all fear war, and the effects of war. You will know of the terrible loss of life and destruction going on in our star system. The whole galaxy is affected. We do not know when it will come, but we know that it is only a matter of time for us.'

Erika's face showed the sadness that everyone on her planet felt about the Orion war. People they knew on other planets were dying, defending their homelands, and more battles were being lost than won. Erika did not ask anything of me, but she turned her face towards a wall, and at her command, a space-portal appeared there. I knew what I had to do.

'Thank you for taking time to talk to me,' I said, bowing, 'I will do what I can.'

I moved towards the portal. As I got closer, Erika's reality began to shimmer and fade, and I was surrounded in grey frequency waves. I knew where I wanted to go, and walking through the grey, oscillating tunnel, I found myself close to the airstrip near Bardon, where Aram, Mardet and Bordur lived. Standing on the ground there, I announced, 'Let all planets in the Orion constellation be selected at sub-atomic particle level, and let all planets selected go Green.'

I felt a shudder go through the ground, and looking up, saw the clouds begin to clear, showing the blue sky and sunlight behind them.

I went to look for Aram. I was in a wooded area, with twisted trees and fallen tree-trunks with ivy climbing over them. There was a noise up above in the sky. A scout ship was coming down too fast, and smoke was coming out of one side. A small figure fell out of the ship.

Suddenly there was a thump, and Aram landed heavily on the ground from above. His scout ship crashed to the ground nearby and burnt up. That should have been the end for Aram, but as the planet had now gone Green, he immediately got perfect health of mind and body and the cleverest brain in the universe, as he landed. So he was not hurt, after all.

Mardet and Bordur came running through a clearing, followed by other soldiers. 'We've found him!' shouted Mardet.

The two men bent to help their fallen friend, but Aram cried, 'It's all right, I'm not hurt. Somehow, I'm not hurt!'

'What happened?' asked Bordur, 'We heard your scout ship was hit.'

'Yes, that's right,' said Aram. 'I knew I had to get back home through the portal, but the ship was burning up. I made it through, but the ship started to break apart, and I fell and lost consciousness. I can't explain how I am standing here. Suddenly, everything feels different.'

'Yes,' said Mardet, 'I feel it too. It's much better than usual. I hope it continues.'

'Somehow, I think it will,' said Bordur.

The three men turned and joined the soldiers waiting nearby. Up until now, their minds had been fixed on war. They had never allowed themselves to think, 'What will we do after it is over?'

Now the possibility of that thought was seeping into their minds, and they let it stay, welcoming its new reality.

My mind moved out into space, to the Orion battlefield where so much carnage had been going on. The noise of thunder had gone. There were no more explosions, no lightning flashes, and the glowing clouds of red smoke were beginning to drift off into space. Soldiers on both sides, in space suits with personal transporters on their backs, were climbing out of their ships and walking towards each other, to touch hands.

'And what about Olvar the Great?' I thought.

I returned to the Alliance Group control room. Olvar was stepping down from the dais where the high tables were located. He took off his helmet and armour, and sat down on a sofa, looking dazed. Then he put his hand on his forehead.

'I must have been mad!' he murmured. 'I could never have won this war. Why did I want to do it? And now, after all the killing, who can ever forgive me?'

An angel appeared.

'You can come with us,' it said. 'In your life you gained many things, but you did not learn to live properly.'

'Yes,' said Olvar, still talking to himself, 'I've failed to understand what life is about.'

'Begin your learning now,' replied the angel.

Two more angels appeared and escorted Olvar out of this reality.

I returned briefly to Erika's palace. The place was full of people dancing and clapping their hands, in a wild frenzy of joy. It had been a long and terrible war, which had left its mark on everyone across the galaxy. The sense of release now, had a dreamlike quality. Crowds of people thronged the streets and public places. You could not tell where Erika was. The queen had disappeared.

But somewhere amongst the crowds, a small figure dressed in grey was laughing, waving her arms and skipping like a carefree child.

DARK MATTERS

After the Orion war, I put electromagnetic travel on the back burner for a while. Then one day, I heard a talk on the radio about Gran Sasso laboratory, which at the time of writing, is the largest underground research centre in the world, specialising in particle physics. It is located under fourteen hundred metres of rock, below Gran Sasso Mountain in Italy. The depth of rock is intended to shield experiments from the effects of cosmic rays.

In 2017, an international collaboration of scientists launched an instrument called Xenon1T to search for dark matter. Dark matter is thought to be a basic ingredient of the universe, but so far it has not been isolated or measured. According to Wikipedia, 'evidence for dark matter comes from calculations showing that many galaxies would fly apart, or that they would not have formed, or would not move as they do, if they did not contain a large amount of unseen matter.'

It sounded as if scientists were close to detecting dark matter in the Italian laboratory, but had not done so yet. It also sounded as if there might be an electromagnetic environment within the laboratory. I am just an old pensioner, who knows nothing about science, but it occurred to me that it might be possible to make dark matter appear within Xenon1T. If I knew more about it, I probably wouldn't have tried. But nothing daunted, I looked up a photograph of Gran Sasso laboratory, and tuning in to its frequency, found myself in there.

It was a huge, dark room, containing a glass structure with several floors, inside which were various types of equipment. The Xenon1T was a large, white, tube-shaped construction that looked like a giant central heating boiler. It was wired up and linked to detection and measuring equipment in near-by rooms. In my invisible form, I selected the interior of the Xenon1T, and said, 'Let the dark matter that scientists are looking for appear inside the Xenon1T.'

My intention was to be helpful, but the result wasn't. There was too much dark matter, and it wasn't stable. It was expanding at a dangerous rate. A loud alarm went off and people started shouting, 'Evacuate the building! Everyone, get out now!' Quickly changing my approach, I announced, 'Make everything safe, and still work as intended.'

Everything went quiet, and a scientist in a white coat climbed up some steps and looked into the Xenon1T, to see what was going on. I looked in too. All I could see was lots of tiny lights, sparkling on and off like Christmas decorations. I decided to introduce myself to the scientist.

'Hello. You were looking for dark matter. Is what you've got what you were looking for?' I asked. The man, whose name was Carlo, replied, 'The container is too full,' He waved his hands in the air. 'Can you put half of it into that back-up machine over there?'

He pointed to another white cylinder nearby. I did as he asked, and the people in the room divided into two teams. They queued up to observe what was going on in the two cylinders. But they seemed uncertain how to proceed.

'They need the cleverest brain in the universe,' I thought.

'Would it help to have enhanced brain power?' I asked Carlo. Carlo thought for a minute.

'Can you try with this lady first please?' he said, pointing to a young woman standing nearby.

The young lady was in fact his partner. I sent her Green energy, and her face lit up. She looked around in astonishment. Then, recalling the criticality of the moment, she stepped forward.

'We need a video recording device for evidence of what we are seeing.'

Carlo took his partner's hand, and the energy passed to him as well. Then I sent it to all the people in the room, so that they would be on the same wavelength.

I created several devices, which recorded what you could see if you looked through the viewing area. The scientists already had plenty of measuring equipment, but I don't think anyone realised that the dark matter would produce such a glistening, sparkling effect. Both teams began working on their tasks with renewed concentration.

'Fine,' I thought. 'No one has complained, so it must be all right.' But as I left, I thought, 'Now that the UK is leaving the EU, it would be good if we had similar opportunities for British scientists. I wonder where would be the best place to put it?'

Tuning into the universal computer, I appeared in the foyer of a pleasant building, which turned out be a science research unit based in Scotland.

'Best person to speak to, please?' I asked, and found myself standing in the office of a scientist called Alan, who was hard at work at his desk. He looked up, with a start.

'Can I help you?' he asked.

'Hello,' I said, 'my name's Martha, and I've just come from the Gran Sasso laboratory, the fast way. I was able to contribute to their work. The UK doesn't have a research base like that, but it would be possible, if you are interested.'

At that moment, I caught sight of myself in a mirror on the wall, and noticed that there were sparkling, fairy lights going on and off around my energy field. In spite of that, Alan took me seriously. He asked me to describe in detail what had happened at the Italian laboratory. Then he said, 'The thing is, Martha, we don't have any people with expertise in that area working in the UK. We do have British people working in the Italian laboratory, but their work is over there. However, I would be willing to go ahead, in principle.'

'Well, that's a start,' I said. 'Would you like the same energy enhancement that they got in the Italian laboratory?'

'Let's all have it! Bring it on, Martha!' said Alan, leaning back in his chair, his hands behind his head.

I sent the Green energy to everyone in the building. A lady outside the door, carrying a tray of tea mugs was taken by surprise. I heard the mugs start to fall, and quickly caught the tray, placing it on a table in the corridor. As usual, I found that these advanced research scientists knew a lot more than they discuss openly. Alan quickly worked out what to do, now that he had the same abilities as I had.

'I can create a lab in the basement under the existing building,' he said, and he went ahead and did that.

He hurried down the back stairs, to check on his work. At the bottom of the stairs, there was now a door, with a glass section at the top so that you could look in. Alan opened the door and went down a staircase into a huge laboratory very like the one in Italy. The lab had identical equipment but no video recording kit. So I recreated the same video recording kit that I had given to Carlo.

Alan got on the phone to other UK scientists that he knew, to ask who they thought would be the best people to come and work in the laboratory. He soon got a call back saying that American scientists were interested and that they could be there in ten minutes!

'Sounds like they are going to travel the fast way too,' I thought.

Sure enough, a whole team of American scientists suddenly appeared in the lab, from nowhere. 'Ah, you must be Alan,' said their team leader, whose name was Owen. Turning to me, he added, 'Nice to meet you, too.'

The Americans inspected the lab and said it was satisfactory.

'And now,' said Owen, 'perhaps our friend could put dark matter into the receptacle.'

So I did that, and the scientists all clustered round, videoing what they could see. I was worried that the lab wasn't fourteen hundred metres underground.

'Won't the research be affected by cosmic rays?' I asked.

'Don't worry, Martha,' said Alan, 'I thought of that, and built in a roof feature that replicates the environment of the Gran Sasso lab, without having to bore down into the rock.'

Having carried out initial checks on the dark matter, the Americans were ready to go. 'Alan, we need to get settled in hotels, can you assist us?'

'Sure,' said Alan, and they went off to sort out their accommodation.

The Americans were already committed to another research project in the States, but they did not want to miss out on working with dark matter. An added bonus was that they were willing to carry out skills transfer to UK scientists as part of the new Scottish project.

I passed on Green energy to the American scientists, and they created a replica site, next door to the new Scottish laboratory, identical to the one they used in the States, so that they could divide their time between the two projects without having to travel. I must admit that I was out of my depth with the science of dark matter, but it seemed to have worked out all right.

INTERGALACTIC SUPPORT GROUP MEETING

Following the discovery of the 'Big Plan for Earth' and the headquarters of the criminal conglomerate on Planet Arturus, diplomatic action had to be taken. There is an Intergalactic committee, where senior figures from planets colonised by Americans over the years, meet every few months to discuss cooperation on trade, defence and harmonisation of standards. A lower-level committee, called the Intergalactic Support Group, exists to deal with bureaucratic communications and preparation of draft papers for the Intergalactic committee.

I wanted to find out what was being done in the aftermath of the Arturus debacle, so I decided to sit in on the Intergalactic Support Group Meeting invisibly. The meeting was held in an electromagnetic building constructed off-Earth, with beaming-up arrangements linked to planets that were members of the Intergalactic committee.

I arrived in the middle of the meeting. There were twenty white men in suits sitting round an oval table. A representative from Planet Arturus, whose name was Elcor, was in the chair for this session. Elcor was speaking, 'Thanks to our friend, our outer galactic trading partners are no longer willing to trade with us. Isn't that right, Deran?'

I realised that the person being referred to as 'our friend' was me. Deran, who represented Planet Igrashel said, 'Yes, that's right. We had a child cultural exchange programme with the Orion group, and since they went a certain colour, they cancelled that and they won't trade with us.'

A man called Harald, sitting at the other end of the table, who came from a planet in the Arturus Group, said, 'It's the same with Orchia and the rest of the Draco group. They won't have any dealings with us until we are Green at subatomic particle level.'

The representative from Planet Atman, whose name was Partur, and whose planet had already gone Green, turned to the Earth representative, whose name was Mark, and said, 'Your people haven't gone Green. Why not?'

'Oh,' said Mark, who came from the US military, 'we have technical security here to exclude electromagnetic intrusions of any sort.'

'I thought your military had people who've gone Green?' said Elcor. Mark looked uncomfortable. He smiled uneasily,

'Well, we do have some, but we have to limit their access, because they tend to raise ethical issues. But we use them where it seems appropriate.'

'Of course,' Elcor continued, 'going Green is not the only way to achieve progress. Our genetic modification breeding programme has produced very clever people, too.'

'What about the "Big Plan for Earth"?' asked Deran, turning to Mark. 'Haven't you guys got very clever people in the US, as a result of that fiasco?'

'Yep,' said Mark, feeling on firmer ground now. 'We've been able to identify all the "plants" from that program, and remotely disconnect them from their handlers. They're all doing well in their professions or in their studies — totally unaware of course.'

'But their parents were in on it,' said Elcor. 'What's being done about that?'

'We have them under observation,' said Mark. 'But there's no evidence that they are doing anything wrong. Under the Big Plan, they'd received all the financial support they needed to get their kids into the right places. But these guys were already making a lot of money in their own right.'

'That just means they were in your Mafia,' said Elcor.

'I think you mean your Mafia, don't you?' said Mark, giving Elcor an "old fashioned" look.'

'Anyway, we can't find a connection between them and any leading politicians at the moment, though with the new wave of cleverer ones in their twenties and thirties, there's no knowing where they'll end up.'

'You don't think that Trump …?' asked a man at the end of the table. All the men laughed.

'No,' said Mark, 'we don't think that. Although the bad guys did say they weren't that satisfied with the performance of "plants" from earlier years of their programme, so you never know. But that would be going back a long way now, forty to fifty years.'

'You don't think that Obama…?' asked Elcor. There was more laughter.

'Well,' continued Elcor, 'he's a bright guy and there was some confusion about his ancestry…'

'No,' replied Mark, 'We don't think that. He got there by himself.'

'Can we get back to our trading and communications issues?' asked Harald. 'What are we going to do about our trading group not being Green enough? Is it possible for you to fix that?'

'Our planet is mixed,' said Mark. 'My understanding is that we are a long way off from achieving a majority of the population wanting to go Green. Which means, it won't happen.'

'But you've got pockets of people who are Green,' said Harald. 'A few of your scientists are Green, I understand. Can't you get them to pass it on to your trading division?'

Mark began to feel under pressure.

'I can't speak for the US, let alone other countries on this,' he said. 'We haven't formulated a policy yet.'

'I heard that there's an embargo on Mars. No one's allowed in, unless they've gone Green,' Harald continued.

'Yes,' said Mark, 'that is true. We are still working with the European Space Agency on those issues. There are plenty of astronauts and scientists who do qualify already, both in North America and Europe.'

'I gather that our friend has given UK scientists an unfair advantage,' said Deran. 'Rumour has it that they can make any materials they wish, without the need for trading. Why can't we all be in that position?'

'Well,' said Elcor, looking at Partur, the Planet Atman representative, 'I hope I'm not speaking out of turn, but some of us may already be in that position.'

'Why are you looking at me?' said Partur. 'This matter has never been discussed here before, and I don't know what our policy is on it.'

'Well, can I suggest that it goes on the agenda for our next meeting?' said Elcor. 'I think Earth is in the chair for that.'

'Oh, OK,' said Mark, in a resigned voice.

'Right,' said Elcor, 'unless anyone has anything else they want to raise, I suggest we leave it at that. Thank you very much for coming everyone. Please keep in touch, if there's anything we need to know, won't you?'

There were murmurs of assent, and the committee members and their bag carriers, who had been sitting around the wall behind them, got up and started to move towards the door, splitting into groups. They went to their respective 'beaming-up' rooms, to return to their home planets.

ASIAN PLANET

In the days that followed, the US Mafia attacks on me intensified. By now, I had got rid of so many terrorists that I thought there could be hardly any left. But they still kept on coming. I went to see the US Military on the Mexican border about it.

'Have a word with the Mexican military over the wall,' said a US border guard. 'I reckon they might just be able to help you there.'

I looked over the electromagnetic wall which defined the border between Mexico and New Mexico. A couple of Mexican military men were standing there.

'She wants to know where the ghouls are coming from,' said the US border guard.

The Mexicans smiled.

'We have more US criminals on our side than they do on theirs,' said one of them. 'What you need to do is call out all the villains living in Mexico. Also, you might like to call out all those originally responsible for the covert war. Lots of them retired to Mexico.'

So I did that, and I removed more terrorists that way than ever before. There must have been over a million. I got rid of so many in the US and Mexico that the Mafia ran out of cash. But their Asian partners, Islamic State, who wanted to continue the European War, decided to buy them out and focus all attention on me.

They still believed that I could be useful to them, if I could just be brought under their control. They began a series of technical attacks designed to raise my blood pressure and reduce my energy to the point that I would not be able to leave the house. The intensity of attacks was increasing, and my health was being affected. I had to deal with the never-ending stream of ghouls. I tuned into the universe.

'Please show me the people behind all this?' I asked.

I found myself in the penthouse suite of a modern building in Pakistan, with thick beige carpets, beige sofas and easy chairs. Several men wearing camel-coloured designer suits were sitting talking. At the back of the open-plan room was a darkened, split-level work area, where Asian technicians worked at desks on laptop computers and other communications devices.

Above the work room was a concealed area, where Californian technical support terrorists were communicating with their colleagues in the States. The whole outfit looked like the hub of a big network stretching across the globe. I was about to move in for the kill, using the command, 'Select all. Dead!' when I was interrupted.

A window appeared in my visual screen and I had a glimpse of a work room inside the US military compound in New York. There were a group of men in uniform, working at desk tops. Sitting closest to the window, one man in his fifties, with grey hair, came into focus in front of them.

'Can you give them to us?' he said.

'No,' I replied.

'Why is the US military superpower asking me for help?' I thought.

'What have you ever done to stop your terrorists from attacking me?' I said. 'Get them yourself.'

'I can't,' replied the man.

Then I realised that the man was stating the truth. US military terms of engagement did not permit them to do certain things in Pakistan, and apparently, extracting US home-grown terrorists was one of them. If they had been in a NATO country, I expect things would have been different.

'Oh, all right,' I said.

I selected all the US Mafia technical support staff and sent them, alive, to the US Military portal in New York. I followed to see where they were from. The woman officer working at the portal read the labels on the ghouls' wrist-bands as they were let in.

'All the labels say "Francisco", she announced. 'Why not San Francisco?'

'Because it isn't "San Francisco",' replied her male colleague. 'It's just "Francisco".'

'What is he on about?' I thought, and I tuned into his mind to see if I could get a better picture. I found myself looking at an advanced covert environment, made of electromagnetic web

structures, positioned underground near Mount Shasta, the well-known mountain in California. 'What did you mean by "just Francisco"?' I asked the US portal guard.

'They are a two-centre organisation, partly in Frisco and partly underground,' he replied.

'How do you know that?' I continued.

'Hell, everyone knows that,' he said. 'If you work here, you soon get to know where they hang out.'

As he spoke, I picked up that he had once been a US Mafia

employee, one of those brought in and rescued — a poacher turned gamekeeper. The US military used them on the portal border control team, because the job did not require too much training, and knowledge of ghouls was considered an advantage. This man must have visited the technical support staff underground hideout near Mount Shasta, which was how he knew about their two-centre headquarters.

I went to check out the Mount Shasta complex. Despite being underground, the structure had a direct light source from outside. The main room was large with a high ceiling, divided into four arched segments like ancient church buildings. There was a room above, where senior staff worked. The main hall was full of men wearing tight, white head coverings that concealed their identity. To judge by the tasks they were engaged in, they were specialists in various electromagnetic, sonic and web-based technologies.

Keeping myself invisible, I searched for the men master-minding these operations. They were upstairs in a semi-darkened room, crouched over a table, with maps and technology devices, discussing troop movements. I put tracking markers on the heads of all the men.

After watching the men for a while, I tried to remove the white face mask of the leader. The face mask was stuck to a wig, and I had to pull them both off together. Underneath, was the head of an ordinary-looking man in his late thirties. If you passed him in a street in California, you wouldn't notice him particularly. The man let out a cry as his wig came off.

At that moment, guided by the tracking markers, armed men in orange workwear, from the US military, broke into the electromagnetic room and put cuffs on the ring leaders. The soldiers had been winched down from an electromagnetic stealth aircraft. They were soon winched up again, each holding a terrorist. I followed them into a purpose-built military personnel carrier. The aircraft had rows of wide seats in pairs, on either side of the gangway. The Navy seals, or whoever they were, put each terrorist in one seat, and sat next to them.

Meanwhile, a group of US military engineers had tunnelled into the base of the electromagnetic building, creating four portals, each of which had a covered way leading up into the military aircraft. Armed US special forces stood around the walls of the hideout, ordering the terrorists into the aircraft, while others put cuffs on the men as they entered the covered walkway. The building was emptied in minutes. Then soldiers began working through every cupboard and filing cabinet, removing the contents in plastic bags. This is the kind of operation that the US military do very effectively.

I wanted to know who was running the underground base. I had met so many of these technical specialists over the years, but I never managed to find their leader.

Tuning into their frequency, I looked for the person driving them, and suddenly, I was on a tropical planet with luxuriant jungle and exotic plants. The air was balmy and relaxing. I could sense the taste of the sea on the breeze, so we were not far from the beach. A Nepalese man with a bald head, wearing a long, terracotta robe, walked slowly, in bare feet, along a jungle path. His name was Nayeem. The path curved downwards, descending in steps. Twenty feet below, there was a weathered patio, with warm, terracotta tiles, a wooden table and wooden chairs. I could hear people talking on the patio.

Nayeem, I discovered, had written books on spiritual guidance and had followers not only in Nepal, but in Pakistan.

He was opposed to abuses of capitalism and saw the cultures of North America and Europe as evil. He was particularly popular with Islamic State terrorists because he did not treat them as terrorists, and did not judge them. The Islamic State terrorists had introduced their US Mafia friends to Nayeem, and it was thanks to the US Mafia technical support group, who beamed him up, that Nayeem now lived on this planet.

The people talking on the patio were three technical support staff from San Francisco. Nayeem called down to them, 'I'm just coming.'

Nayeem sat down at the head of the table. Turning to the head of the Mafia group, he said, 'So, your people have been taken by the US military?'

'Yes,' replied the Californian, 'there are few of us left. Can you help us? We need more support.'

'The Terramarsh are expected,' said Nayeem.

'We are here now,' a voice announced.

Five tall human figures, wearing dragon helmets with visors, emerged from the doorway of a space vehicle which stood concealed nearby in the jungle. These people came from Earth long ago, but now lived on a different planet which they shared with many other races.

'We are not late, but we waited for you to arrive. So now we are here,' said the leading Terramarsh. The five figures stood staring at the seated group.

'Our friends have suffered losses at the hands of the US military,' said Nayeem. Aschotel, the leader of the Terramarsch spoke.

'We should take *her*. We can do it. We will come now.'

'No!' said Nayeem. 'She is too powerful. You can't take her out.'

'She is one woman. It can be done,' replied Aschotel.

'No!' repeated Nayeem. 'It's been tried. It doesn't work. For God's sake man, she has Asian angels helping her. Do you expect to win? I tell you, I would give a lot to see an Asian angel myself.'

'Then we will carry on alone,' said Aschotel.

The five men turned and walked back into their spacecraft. The ship was vertical, with convoluted corridors leading to each seat. Once they had all taken their places, the vehicle disappeared. I never saw them again, and if they tried to enter Earth's atmosphere, they would be automatically re-routed to the US military portal.

Nayeem turned to the Californians.

'My friends, the time is not right for you to continue the fight. My advice is, lie low. Find a new home for your group. Build up your strength. The time will come when you can fight again. Now go.'

The three Californians got up and left, using a beaming-up facility. Finally, Nayeem was alone. He looked up, searching the sky. A giant brown angel with cream robes and wings appeared and hovered above him, looking down with deep compassion. Nayeem was transfixed by the angel. Since an angel had chosen to show up, I decided to appear. The angel looked at me.

'Do you want me to make this planet go Green?' I asked

'Yes,' said the brown angel, who was now standing on the ground.

I turned the planet Green at subatomic level. Nayeem breathed out a sigh, as he was transformed. Then he ran towards the angel with his arms outstretched. The angel enfolded him in its wings.

'We will come and look after you now,' said the angel.

At that moment, a large number of brown angels appeared, flying over the hills. 'I wish all my people from Earth could be here,' said Nayeem.

I looked at the angel.

'Shall I bring them?' I asked.

'Yes,' said the angel.

I didn't need to know who Nayeem meant by "all my people".' I just took whatever he meant by that phrase, and said, 'Select "all my people".'

Then I gathered them all in a huge net and brought them to the planet. There were thousands of them, from Nepal and Pakistan. They arrived just as they were, some in rags, some carrying rifles, some in Asian clothes and some in Eurasian clothes. But as soon as they landed on the ground, the Green power of the planet took over, and they were transformed.

Angels flew in and started their work, talking with, supporting and caring for their new charges. From now on, these Asians had guardian angels. They would never suffer pain, sickness or old age, and they would never lack for anything ever again.

After that, whenever I met Asian terrorists, I sent them straight to the Asian planet. I also created a command that Asians could use to take themselves there, just by saying, 'I want to Go Green.' Not wanting to lose their work force, the Asian top brass forbade their troops to use this command. But word soon word got around amongst the Asians. They would volunteer to come and support the US Mafia just to get the opportunity of being sent to the Asian planet.

The first time that happened, a group of forty Islamic State warriors beamed themselves across to the US Mafia operations base in New Mexico. The US Mafia wanted them to attack me via electromagnetic corridors they had constructed from the States. I was watching in the New Mexico

arena as the Asians arrived. The Asian commander saw me and called two of his soldiers forward. He nodded to them, and they stated their wish to go to their new planet, using the request:

'I want to go Green.'

With a whoosh, they were gone. I followed them to the Asian planet and found them on a beach looking out on a bay. A minute later, their commander joined them. Then a brown angel appeared.

'Why don't you bring all your troops?' the angel asked the commander.

The commander selected all his men mentally, and willed them to go Green. Suddenly the beach was full of soldiers.

'These are my men,' said the commander, 'but in Pakistan there are so many that I do not know and cannot bring.'

The angel turned to me and said, 'Can you bring them?'

I selected all the ghouls in Pakistan who were on the electromagnetic computer system at that time, and sent them to the planet. There were thousands of them flying in on the horizon. As they appeared, angels joined them, welcoming them and guiding them to different locations.

As I was writing this, Asian terrorists living underground in New Mexico were listening in. I heard an Asian child's voice. 'I haven't seen angels. I want to see angels.'

There were children in the New Mexico Asian group, listening to my "story".' I looked across and saw about twenty Asian kids under twelve years of age. At that moment, a large brown angel with cream wings appeared in New Mexico, wearing white robes. The angel swooped down. 'Hello lovelies, come with me.'

It scooped all the children up and flew off with them.

In the end, I created a command which meant that every time Asians got put onto the terrorists' electromagnetic computer system, they went to their planet immediately. Since that time, I have not seen any Asian terrorists in the electromagnetic environment on Earth.

I went back to my home. All was quiet. Then forty black terrorists were driven into the arena. They looked confused and afraid. Having lost Asian support, the US Mafia had temporarily dumped black recruits in the arena to keep the war going, until they sorted out what to do next.

The black recruits were in their ordinary clothes. They had not even been given protective uniforms. Many of them came from disadvantaged backgrounds. Having become terrorists, there was no way back for them. They were usually recruited in prison, and told that when they came out, if they went to a certain place, there would be a job for them.

Since brown angels had started a planet for Asian terrorists, black angels might be interested in doing the same for black terrorists. I went out into space, and asked to speak to a black Angel. Several angels of different colours appeared, including black angels. They already knew what I wanted to ask.

'Is there a place for black terrorists to go?' I asked. 'Follow us,' said the black angels.

They flew off, cutting through the universe at speed. Soon, a planet with canopies of green trees came into sight. The black angels landed in a large, grassy clearing, with the sun streaming through.

'Let's make this our home for all the poor people we want to pick up and rescue,' said one Angel.

'Will it be like the black angels' planet for little kids that I once saw before?' I asked.

'Not quite like that,' said the angel. 'We want to start a new life for all those we want to help.' I looked across a wide landscape of mountains and hills, with lakes in the valleys.

'Let's start here,' said the angel. 'We can wait while you turn the planet Green.'

I sent the planet the Green energy. Immediately, more black angels with golden wings appeared in the sky. I left the angels and went back to where the black terrorists were sitting round talking.

'The Asians have gone. We don't see them any more,' said one young man, 'brown angels took them.'

I joined the group of men.

'There are black angels too,' I said. 'I've been to a planet where they act as guardians to black kids.'

'What's this about black angels?' asked one of the men. 'I never heard of them,' said another

As they talked, a huge black angel with cream-coloured wings appeared in the sky and looked down.

'Look, there's one now!' cried the young man.

All the men looked up. The black angel was smiling broadly and holding a packet of potato chips. He took one out and ate it. Then he flew over to the group of black guys and dropped a potato chip into each of their hands. They just stood there staring for a moment. Then one of them spoke. 'There *is* such a thing as a black angel! We have our own angels looking out for us!' The men's faces changed from despondency to hope.

'This guy seems to care about us,' said another man.

The giant angel flew down and put his arms around the group of men. 'I am your momma and your poppa,' said the angel.

The black guys were filled with amazement.

'Can we marry you and live with you forever?' asked one of them.

The black angel looked at me and telepathically said, 'OK, you can turn them Green now.'

I was going to do it earlier, but I sensed that the angel wanted me to hold back 'til it had introduced itself. As I turned everyone Green, the angel picked them up in his arms, and flew off to their new planet.

FALL OF THE GHOULS

So now there were planets for Asian and black terrorists to have a new start in life.

'Perhaps there ought to be a planet for all other terrorists who had never had a chance on Earth,' I thought.

I went out into space and looked for some angels. I had to go up into the higher dimensions of the universe to find them, where it was no longer dark. Then I saw a group of white, black and brown angels talking together about the new planets. They looked up when I appeared.

'Do you think there should be a planet for terrorists who aren't Asian or black as well?' I asked.

'No!' said a black angel, 'The rest of the human species, as it is on Earth, is unique to that planet, and should stay there. They don't need anywhere else to go.'

'Definitely not!' said a brown angel. 'They are the ones causing all the trouble on Earth.'

'Hmm,' I thought. 'I'm not sure that humans started the trouble.'

My mind went back to the sulky-looking fallen angels who decided to build their replacement kingdom on Earth. They lost their angelic powers and needed others to do their dirty work for them. This was why they got their hooks into people on Earth. They were behind the creation of the intergalactic criminal alliance, known as the "Joint Galactic

Sharing Agreement" It was under this agreement that the US Mafia were able to call on villains from other planets to help them in their war on Earth.

Just then a large white angel with cream wings joined the group.

'Look over there,' it said, pointing to a sparkling star, shining in the dawn sky.

As I watched, the star started to change size. It got bigger. Then it became egg-shaped, and finally spherical. It glowed with an opaque, white radiance.

'The rest of the human ghouls can go there,' said the large white angel, smiling.

'Oh thanks!' I cried.

After turning the planet Green, I announced. 'Let all terrorist ghouls who are not black or Asian, and who want a new start in life go to the new planet.'

As I spoke, thousands of dirty, ragged-looking terrorists began streaming towards the new planet. At the same time, a flock of white angels appeared, accompanying their new charges.

I thought about all the terrorists who had died over the years, mainly because their gang-masters had forced them onto the battlefield.

'Would it be possible for terrorists who never had a chance in their life, and who are already dead, to still go to their planets now?' I asked.

'Why not? I like that idea,' said a black angel.

'Let's get started,' said a brown angel.

So I made an announcement about ghouls that were already dead. Then I heard a noise behind me, and as I turned round, I saw four white angels dragging the ends of a large net through space. Inside the net were a vast number of wriggling grey and brown figures, tossing and turning and crying out, 'I wasn't me. I didn't do it. I never touched them. Help me, someone!'

The poor creatures seemed unaware of what was going on around them. Perhaps they were still reliving a hell that they had come from. Then another four angels appeared, towing a net full of recently-rescued French Canadians. The men were chuckling with pleasure, exchanging conspiratorial glances, as they were not sure they were allowed to speak in the presence of such high beings.

'We're having a good day, aren't we?' said one of them, nudging another with his elbow. 'An angel at every end!'

The white angels gave amused smiles, as they towed the Canadians to their new planet. There would be plenty of guardian-ing work for them after this.

I arranged it that whenever the ghouls were put onto the terrorist computer system by their gang-masters, they would automatically go straight to their new planets. Word got round about this, and there were queues of low-ranking terrorists waiting patiently for their chance of a new life outside Earth.

A young technician whose job was to put terrorists on to the system, worked overtime, encouraging as many people as possible to step up for their turn. As each one went onto the system, they shot into the air, and disappeared. But any hardened villains who tried it on found themselves going fast in another direction. While this was happening, a white-robed Angel stood by watching. The angel said to the young technician, 'Now it's your turn.'

At the angel's command, the queue stepped back to let the young man onto the system. But before this could happen, the angel picked him up in its arms and carried him away like a small child.

Another young man was watching. How he longed to have an angel carry him like that too! 'I'll work on the system admissions,' he volunteered.

He worked away, admitting people onto the system. The angel had returned by now and was watching again. After a while, the young man looked up at the angel and asked, 'Can I be next on the system now?'

The angel nodded, but did not scoop him up. Everyone who went onto the system got rescued automatically, so it wasn't necessary. But the young man's heart sank. His hopes were dashed, and he burst into tears, covering his eyes like a small child.

Then the angel bent down, picked him up, and carried him away, murmuring, 'There, there,' as the lad sobbed on its shoulder.

A twelve-year old boy from the ultrasound staff side had been watching the terrorists queuing up to be rescued. His boss had told him that ultrasound staff were too evil to get rescued, to prevent him from trying. He stood on a rock looking up at the angel.

'Is there any chance for us evil ones?' he asked. The angel looked down and smiled.

'Why not try and see,' it said encouragingly.

The young boy walked over to the main computer admissions area and asked to go onto the system. He rose up into the air and stood suspended there. The angel joined him, and they disappeared into the sky together.

Shortly afterwards, a group of senior ranking US people-traffickers and weapons-group managers, operating within the ultrasound environment, appeared. They'd heard that their staff — or slaves — had been given their own planet, where they could be happy. Now the bosses wanted to muscle-in on the scene. The chief people-trafficker stood up and shouted at the top of his voice, 'I want to go to my planet! I want to go now! If my staff have gone there, I should be there too.' Immediately a white-robed angel appeared, looking down into the arena. Next to the angel

crouched two beings I had never seen before. They were dark red, with pointed faces, and horns like goats' horns, coming out of their heads, and they held small tridents. It looked as if those tridents were for crowd control purposes. Yes. They were devils!

The angel turned to one of the devils, and said, 'I think you will have to take them. We can't do anything with them.'

The two devils leapt into the pit. One of them picked up the chief people-trafficker by the hair, and stuffed him into a large bag. They started grabbing several weapons-group managers by the hair at once, and bagging them up too. They operated calmly and efficiently, as if it was all in a day's work for them, like municipal refuse bin collectors. Then they walked off into the sunset, their pointed tails shining in the last sun's rays, dragging two very large bags along the ground. And the direction they were going in was definitely down.

A number of junior ultrasound staff were watching. When the chief weapons-group manager got bagged up, they shouted, 'Our Monster Rat's been hit!'

They scurried around, trying to find a place to hide, where they could watch what was going on. I turned to the angel and asked, 'Who are those red beings... Are they devils?'

'They are co-workers with us,' replied the angel. 'We call

them angels of the dark.'

'If they are angels, I ought to send them Green energy,' I thought, so I did.

As soon as they went Green, the devils pulled off their outfits, revealing that they were angelic looking underneath.

'At last, we can regain our forms,' said one of them.

The angels of the dark continued their work as before, but they had been released from an outdated requirement to wear antiquated uniforms at all times. *10

I created a voice command which sent low-frequency ghouls to where the people-traffickers had gone. After that, weapons group managers and people traffickers started falling off their perches all over the place. There were cries of astonishment from lower ranking staff as all their gang-masters disappeared. They were never seen again.

After that, the realm of ghouls, where humans were transformed into something less human, started to disintegrate. Once the top bosses were dead, the junior staff could be heard celebrating. They put on their favourite music, which they had "borrowed" from my iPad playlists. This included *Road to Nowhere* by Talking Heads, which US terrorists used on their junior training courses, and the sombre *Standing at the Sky's Edge* by Richard Hawley. All the terrorists liked that one, because it resonated with what life felt like for them.

There had to be a bad guy behind all the ghouls. Their top management belonged to an obnoxious secret cult, which believed that they were descended from aliens, and that very soon, their ancestors were coming back to Earth, to give them power over everyone. I went looking for the head man, and found myself on a different planet, where a shabbily dressed man in his late fifties was standing.

'Are you the leader of the people traffickers?' I asked.
'Yes,' the man replied.

'Do you control your staff on Earth from here?' I continued.

'Oh no,' said the man. 'I take orders from my god. He decides everything, and I just pass it on to my staff on Earth.'

It turned out that the inner circle of the secret cult had been beamed-up to this planet by their technical support staff, where they were given brain implants to enable them to channel their alien god.

'Who is your god?' I asked.

'His name is Baal-Zebub,' the man replied.

'Right!' I thought. 'That name rings a bell.'

It sounded very like the name of a Philistine god, called Beelzebub. 'Let Baal-Zebub appear,' I announced.

A huge, heavily-built, very rough man appeared, shouting obscenities. He was wearing human clothes, but I couldn't help noticing that he had a tail. He might be big, but with such a low frequency, that made him weak, compared to us humans. We may not be angels, but there is definitely a role for us in cleaning up the universe.

'Let this person go where the people-traffickers have gone,' I said.

The gross figure went hurtling down towards the horizon, still shouting unprintable words. 'Select all planets occupied by that person and his people traffickers, at subatomic particle level, and let them go Green,' I announced.

At that moment, a huge hole opened up in the ground on the planet, about a quarter of a mile wide. A mass of black bats was disgorged from the hole, and hurled out into space. The bats headed straight for Earth. As they landed, they changed shape, and became senior management people-trafficker ghouls.

The first thing they did was to construct electromagnetic architecture inside the Earth's atmosphere, where they could hide. I watched as one of the shapeshifters took its place as the manager in the electromagnetic arena around my house. He looked just like any ghouls' manager, but I knew better.

'You're a bat, aren't you?' I said accusingly.

Hearing himself named and shamed destabilised the malevolent alien, and he threw his head back and let out a series of terrible howls. Then sharp teeth extended out of his mouth, and he lost his human appearance completely, morphing back into a black, leather-winged spirit. He rose to the ceiling, flapping furiously trying to find the way out.

'Let all bats, on and off-planet, go to the place where the dark angels put the people-traffickers,' I announced.

The bat was knocked sideways and went hurtling over the horizon. It took a while before I got the rest of his crowd sent down to the place where the first lot of people traffickers had gone. But it was worth it.

There were still plenty of Mafia villains and terrorists operating electromagnetic, electronic and sonic weapons in the outside world. I will not pretend that ghouls never got created again, but their day was over, and they were no longer a serious force to be reckoned with.

LIFE IN A HIGHER DIMENSION

One morning, after a week of continuous attacks from local British and Irish terrorists, I got up, had breakfast, and went back to bed to listen to music for a while. But the terrorists were still trying to get my attention.

'Let all my previous commands in existence be repeated every billionth of a second!' I shouted. The terrorists crumbled into dust and faded away. My eyes closed, but I was awake. I watched the darkness clear, and found myself looking down on Earth from space. It was quite cluttered with space stations and satellites. Suddenly, two large jet planes appeared, steering a path between all the objects above Earth. The aircraft were petrol-blue in colour, and looked inviting. It was crazy, but I jumped into one of them and sat in a seat at the back of an aircraft.

The aircraft was empty, apart from myself and two air hostesses cooking in the galley. They were microwaving food to be served as soon as the aircraft took on passengers at the next stop. They were smartly dressed in knee-length, red suits, and looked very elegant. I realised I would need to upgrade my image, and mentally changed my clothes into whatever was acceptable to the people I was with.

One of the hostesses came over and asked to see my boarding pass. I mentally created whatever she would expect to see. As I handed it to her, I noticed that the destination read

"SUTOR." The air hostess examined the boarding pass and said, 'You will need to change at the next airport stopover. I will help you to find your way when we get there.'

That was great, so I sank back in my seat and relaxed, looking out of the window at stars and plasma dust clouds. We passed close to a moon, pock-marked with craters, which shone eerily in the half-light of a distant star. It never occurred to me to think, 'What is a jet plane doing in outer space, and how can it land on a different planet?'

Soon it was time to land. As we descended, the view from my window disappeared, and was replaced by darkness. It was night and I could hardly make out what the planet looked like until the we reached the lights of the airstrip and airport buildings. As we landed, a huge, transparent, plastic shell came out of the roof of the buildings and covered the runway.

The air hostess handed me a transparent helmet, and explained how to put it on, because the air outside was not safe to breath. We all went down the aircraft steps and walked into the building. Once in the building, we removed our helmets and handed them to a stewardess. The stewardess checked my boarding card, and pointed to a leisure area with sofas and easy chairs.

'Go and wait there,' she said. 'Your name will be called when it is time to embark.'

A line of passengers wearing helmets walked out of the building towards the plane I had just got off, escorted by more smart air hostesses. Then my name was called, and I went forward to the boarding gate, where I was handed another helmet, and told to go to a different aircraft waiting on the tarmac.

I was shown to a seat by a hostess, who took my helmet

and put it on the rack above my head. The back of the seat in front of me unfolded to reveal a wine glass, knife, fork and side plate. A meal was served. Most of the passengers chose what looked like beef wellington, but I opted for cheese and spinach pasta.

Soon we were approaching a planet surrounded in soft, white cloud. It was called Sutor. It glowed in the light of a nearby sun. As we entered its atmosphere, sparks flew for a minute, but the plane was unharmed. We coasted over a pale blue sea, and landed normally on a runway.

We descended an escalator onto the tarmac. No helmets were needed now. An air hostess guided me into the airport buildings and pointed to a helpdesk, where I could order a courtesy taxi to take me to a hotel.

Within an hour, I was checking in at the hotel foyer. The receptionist asked for my credit card. I pretended to look in my bag, and mentally created a card that would work at the hotel. Unbelievably, it was accepted. The receptionist asked where my luggage was. Again, I pretended to look for it, and mentally created a suitcase containing everything I would need for my stay. Soon, I was in a comfortable room, with a lovely window looking over a bay. I got into bed and fell asleep immediately.

Next morning, I went down to breakfast wearing a formal, navy suit, with a short jacket. In the foyer, I was stopped by a gentleman wearing hotel uniform, who asked me if I would like to arrange a programme of tours during my stay. I agreed, and it went on the bill. Then my tour guide, Felix, arrived. He was a fit young man, in his twenties. He took a look at my outfit, and advised me to change into something more relaxed.

'What does he have in mind?' I thought.

As soon as I got to my room, I mentally created an outfit

that he would find acceptable. It was a pale-blue cashmere twinset, with matching blue trousers, and light, summer shoes with strong man-made soles.

'That's much better,' he said approvingly.

We drove through green, rolling countryside until the land started to look parched and dry. Then we were in a desert of bleached-beige sand, with high dunes in the background. We got out and looked across the plain, and down into a ravine below. There were sand-coloured things moving down there — large things. I realised that they were giant snakes, with heads the size of a small car, and bodies just as wide, that went on for twenty-five yards. They didn't do much, just slithered about enjoying their social life. Then we went to a forest filled with brilliantly-coloured macaws, red, blue and green, all squawking loudly.

In the car, on the way back to the hotel, Felix told me he was studying anthropology at college, and that he did guided tours to 'give back something to the community.'

'What do you mean?' I asked.

'We don't have to pay for things in money here,' explained Felix. 'It is all based on how many hours of our time we give to community service. My tuition is free, but if I want to buy things like sports equipment, it is based on the amount of time I have put into doing work for the community.'

When we got back to the hotel. Felix took out a device which looked like a smart phone. Calling up a blank screen, he asked me to write a tip for him, which would be credited to his account in minutes.

'Would you mind?' he said, 'I know you're a visitor, so you're not used to this, but anything would be appreciated.'

I hadn't a clue what to write, but I mentally created an

entry that would be what he wanted the tip to be. It worked. Felix gave me a big smile, and wished me a pleasant stay.

Next day, an elegant young lady called Elena was waiting to take me on a tour of riverside scenery ending up at the sea. We looked at waterfalls and dams. I walked across a dam, from which you could see a panorama of hills and valleys with green and silver trees. Then we followed the river into an estuary, where it joined the sea. We stopped at a building which had a series of conservatories, from which you could watch the river flowing into the sea. Where the river met the sea, there was a rise in the water, as the water-flows found their way round each other.

Elena took me to a viewing point where I could sit in an armchair, and she went to order tea. While she was gone, a Scottish gentleman in his early sixties, called Don, wearing a beige tweed jacket, brown tweed trousers and a green jumper came and sat down in an armchair opposite me. He looked at me for a moment, and then he asked, 'Are you from Earth?'

'Yes,' I said, 'how did you know?'

Don smiled a kind, understanding smile.

'I can tell from the suffering in your face. We don't have suffering here.'

Elena appeared, pushing a tea trolley, and Don got up and offered her his seat. After he left, I began thinking about what he had said. That night, in my room I suddenly realised.

'Of course! We are in a higher dimension. That must be why jet planes could fly past Earth without being seen. There are people living their lives in higher bandwidths, that we cannot detect from our level of existence.'

When we sleep, we don't normally suffer fear or pain, and everything is peaceful. And that is exactly how it was on this planet. Everything had a peaceful, dream-like easiness about it. All the people I met were kind and caring, and nothing really went wrong.

Next day, Don came to see me at the hotel, accompanied by his friend Angus. Both of them were originally from Scotland. They brought me a beautiful plant with white flowers in a pot, and asked me to join them for tea, at the same place as I met Don the day before. I had the impression that they were able to read my thoughts, though they did not say so.

'Perhaps telepathy is normal on this planet?' I thought.

Don and Angus came to collect me from the hotel for tea. But first, they wanted to show me where they lived. Their houses were next to each other in a quiet cul-de-sac. The buildings had red, sloping tiled roofs and semi-circular, red wall tiles, lining the walls of the houses. Don had a walled garden, and a large, glass conservatory leading into his house. The conservatory was full of flowering plants of different colours, including white ones like the one he had given me.

Then we went to the tea rooms which looked out on the estuary. Elena was there again. She brought sandwiches and cakes on a trolley. Don and Angus made a point of not asking personal questions.

'Will they be interested if I tell them about going Green?' I thought. 'They are practically there already.'

But going Green would mean that nobody would have to work for a living, and everyone could enjoy even more freedom in how they lived their lives.

Don looked at me enquiringly, as if to say, 'Well, we're waiting. When are you going to speak?' So I did.

'You have a lovely life here,' I said, 'but have you ever

thought what it would be like if you were able to create everything you wanted, without having to work?'

'I don't mind having to work,' said Elena, helping herself to a sandwich, 'I like it.'

Don and Angus looked at each other for a moment. Then Don said, 'You know, I've always wanted there to be a bridge over the estuary, so that you could walk onto it, and watch the river flowing under it.'

I took the image Don had in his mind and put it across the estuary. 'You mean, like that?' I said.

Don looked at it.

'Yes, but not quite there.'

'Let the bridge be as Don wants it, where he wants it,' I thought.

'Yes, that's right now,' said Don.

He and Angus got up and went out onto the bridge. They started looking at the water flowing under it, and admiring the view across the bay and up the river. Then they came back and sat down.

'It would be possible for your whole planet to work like that,' I said.

'You mean everyone could have the powers to create what they want?' asked Don.

'Yes,' I said.

'How would that work?' asked Angus.

'If your planet was completely transformed, the moment anyone set foot on it for the first time, they would be changed, and would be able to create things,' I explained.

Then I remembered how the planet of the ruffians had gone Green, and how angels had appeared.

'There might be more to it than that,' I added. 'How would

you feel if high frequency beings appeared. I mean, like angels, perhaps?'

Don smiled.

'We have them already,' he said. 'Informally, that is.'

'All right,' I thought. 'These people have been having a joke all along. If they know all this, they must have realised everything about me from the beginning.'

'Well, would you like to try the experience?' I asked. Don looked at me.

'Go on then,' he said.

So I selected him in my mind and thought, 'Go Green.'

Don gasped and sat back in his chair. I had completely forgotten to mention about having the cleverest brain in the universe and perfect health of mind and body.

Angus stared at Don intently. 'What has happened?' he asked.

'You can pass it on to others by touching them on the arm,' I said. Immediately, Don touched Angus on the arm, and he sat back gasping as well. 'Can you give it to me please?' asked Elena.

I thought 'Go Green' to Elena, forgetting that you might need to be sitting down, as the experience can take you by surprise. Elena fell backwards and ended up sitting on the floor. I sent Elena an energy beam to fix any damage.

'It's OK. I'm not hurt,' said Elena, laughing.

'Well, what do you think?' I asked Don. 'Do you think people on your planet would like to have this experience?'

'Let's go and ask them,' said Don.

He got up and walked to a door at the end of the room. As he opened it, a murmur of voices came out, and I could see men sitting round long tables and on window-seats lining the room. It was a cross between a golf club bar and a parliamentary meeting room. Perhaps this group of men in their sixties had a role in the government of their country. I cannot overlook the fact that it was all men, with no women represented, but if this planet started up in the 1960s and hadn't changed much, that might explain it.

'Let's go in,' said Don.

'Can I come too?' asked Elena.

'Of course,' Don said.

Don made his way to a table on a raised step at one end of the room. He took a knife and used it to ring a note on a glass. The voices subsided and everyone turned to look at him.

'Listen everyone, we have a visitor here with something to say,' he announced. Then, turning to me, with a gesture of his arm, he said, 'Martha, you're on.'

I stood up and introduced myself.

'Hello everyone, as Don says, I am a visitor to your land, and I am here to tell you that there is an opportunity that can benefit your planet and everyone on it, if you feel it would be a good thing for you.'

'It's already happened to me,' said Don.

'What are we talking about, please?' said one of the men.

'The cleverest brain in the universe, perfect health of mind and body, and the ability to create from mind whatever you wish. It is a high frequency ability, so it cannot be used to do harm, though like everything else, it has to be used with consideration for others,' I said.

'It can be passed on just by touching,' said Angus.

'Give it to me then,' said the man next to him.

So Angus touched his arm. 'Me too!' shouted some others.

Don and Angus reached out to touch the men within reach,

and they in turn, passed it on to others. There was noise and commotion around the room, as everyone started to take in what had happened to them.

'Did I hear you say we could create from mind?' said a man. 'If so, can I create another beer?' He raised his empty glass and to everyone's amazement, it filled with golden-brown liquid.

'Go on, try it,' I said. 'You'll find it's the best drink you ever tasted, and it cannot make you drunk. In fact, it will give you whatever vitamins and minerals your body needs.'

The man took a sip. Then he smiled, and took a long drink. 'It is the best I've ever tasted,' he confirmed.

Soon, everyone was trying out their abilities to create food and drink. Don stood up.

'So, everyone,' he said. 'What do you think? Would you like our planet to benefit from this gift, now that you have an idea of what we are talking about? Can I ask for a show of hands? Those in favour please indicate.'

Everyone in the room raised their hands.

'Right, Martha, I think you can go ahead,' said Don. I stood up and announced, 'Let every subatomic particle on this planet now go Green.'

There was a sudden crash outside in the road leading to the building. A vintage car had bumped into a modern one going the other way. Quickly, I added, 'Let going Green cause no harm or inconvenience to anyone, and do no damage to property, retrospectively.'

So the two cars in the road hadn't collided after all, and no one was at all shaken or hurt. But everyone could tell that the planet had changed. I looked up, and through the ceiling. I could see angels gathering on the roof. It was time for me to go home. Elena took me back to the hotel. As I left, Don waved and shouted, 'When are you going to come and live here?'

'I'd love to,' I said, and I meant it. 'But I can't come here in my physical body, which is on Earth, so I will just have to say 'Til we meet again.'

And so, after settling up at the hotel, I returned home to Earth, which though beautiful in so many ways, still included pain and suffering in its experience.

POLITICIANS GET INVOLVED

On my return from Planet Sutor, I began thinking about other people in the Western World, who, like me, were being targeted by terrorists. Despite the constant involvement of the US military and the daily overhead support of the Royal Air Force in the UK, the situation of victims of covert targeting had not improved.

At the end of *Kiss Terror Goodbye*, military security staff at the Pentagon implied that the difficulty lay with politicians, who did not understand the issues. I now began to think that the reason politicians did not understand the issues was that their military heads did not choose to inform them what the issues were.

The main problem was, that the electromagnetic terrorist technologies used by the US Mafia, Islamic State and Irish Republican Army were the same as those used by the US military and NASA for deep space exploration, particularly for "beaming-up" to planets across the universe. So acknowledging the first would mean revealing the second.

I wanted politicians to be involved. After all, if the people's elected representatives were being kept in the dark about how public money was being spent on deep space exploration, something had gone wrong with the democratic process. So, I decided to find a way to involve senior politicians in the United States, British Isles and European

Union. Tuning into the universal computer, I announced, 'Let all members of the following committees receive the same targeting attacks as I do.'

Then I listed the names of a US Senate committee, a UK parliamentary committee, their equivalents in EU member states and an EU parliamentary committee. The committees covered topics such as intelligence, security, defence, crime, terrorism and space transport. Representatives of these committees would all have clearance for information with high security classifications.

The first person I made contact with was Howard, the head of a UK parliamentary committee. Thin and wiry, and wearing a dark suit, he was in his late sixties, at the end of a long and distinguished career. As soon as he was targeted by the terrorists, he was placed in quarantine by the British security services, along with the rest of his committee, close to the Palace of Westminster, in the basement of an old government building. The rooms were lined with wood panels, and were rather dark.

As I arrived, both he and I were shot in the foot by terrorists operating in the British Isles, who had been hired by the Irish Mafia. A member of the UK security services on duty stood by watching impassively.

'Hello, who are you?' asked Howard, clutching his foot.

'I'm Martha, the person whose experiences you are sharing,' I replied. 'It must be confusing at first, not knowing what is going on. You could try searching the internet for "targeted individuals" if you want more information.'

'What I want to know is, who's behind it?' said Howard.

'It's a coalition of the US Mafia, the Irish Mafia and Islamic State, who want to bring down the Western World covertly,' I said, realising how unlikely this must sound.

'How long have you been targeted?' asked Howard.

'Over seven years,' I said. 'But other people in Europe and the United States have been targeted for much longer than that.'

'That doesn't sound good,' Howard muttered, as if talking to himself.

Turning to the security serviceman on duty he announced, 'I want a full explanation from our Special Services people. Please take me to the person in charge here.'

The security officer escorted Howard along a corridor into a large room, where a senior intelligence officer, whose name was Paul, was sitting at a desk. When I caught up with the conversation, Howard was saying.

'British citizens are being targeted.'

'Yes, I know,' replied Paul.

'Why didn't you tell us? What right have you to withhold this information from our committee?' asked Howard.

'There were difficulties in getting American agreement on the way forward, if we did that,' replied Paul.

'The IRA have been doing this on British soil. You knew this, and you didn't stop them. Why not?' demanded Howard.

'I know,' said Paul, and he put his head face down on the desk.

Pauls' hand reached into a small compartment inside his desk. There was the sound of a gun going off, and a bullet went through his heart. As he did this, security staff rushed forward to provide assistance, while others called for an ambulance.

Howard stood there looking totally shocked. I quickly sent energy to Paul, and he came round, his bullet wound gone. At that moment, paramedics came running in to take Paul to hospital.

'It's OK, I'm fine now,' he said.

'What about all that blood on the chair?' asked a paramedic, pointing to a pool of dark liquid staining the brown leather seat.

I removed it.

'There isn't any,' said Paul.

The ambulance crew withdrew. After they had gone, the security staff picked up the bullet, which was lying on the floor, and retrieved the gun.

'You need a rest,' I said to Paul.

'I can't. My boss won't understand,' he replied.

I tuned into the frequency of Paul's boss, and went straight to his office, making myself invisible. Two security men were being shown in to see him.

'Perhaps if I send the boss Green energy, he may be more receptive,' I thought.

So I did that. The boss looked pleasantly surprised. He sat smiling quietly to himself, and welcomed the two security men when they arrived.

'It's not good news, Sir,' said one of them, hesitantly. 'Paul's been shot, by his own gun. But he's had a lucky escape and he's all right now. He's still at work...'

'Oh, poor man, I must speak to him,' said the boss. He picked up the phone.

'Paul, how are you, old chap? Listen, you've been overworking. We can't have this. We must give you more staff, with all that extra work. Don't worry about it. You rest up. Can we meet tomorrow? Fix a time.'

Keeping my invisibility, I went back to Paul, as he came off the phone. He was shaking his head. 'I can't believe it. He was all right about it,' he said.

I decided to send Green energy to Paul too, since his boss already had it. Howard, who was now sitting opposite Paul, stared at him with interest.

'Something's happened to you. What is it?' he asked.

'I'm not sure. I can't exactly say,' said Paul.

At this moment, I reappeared.

'I think you should turn in for the night,' I said to Howard.

'Is there a place for me to sleep?' Howard asked Paul.

'Yes,' said Paul, 'It's just across the corridor.'

He touched Howard on the arm, to guide him in the right direction, and passed the Green energy to him. Howard stepped back, his face lightening up and his body instantly refreshed.

'You passed that to me by touching. Do you realise that?' he asked.

The two men left the room and went down the corridor to Howard's sleeping quarters. As they left, I became aware of someone requesting to make contact with me from an electromagnetic environment above. I looked up and saw a senior man sitting at a desk. I knew I was looking at a high-up Russian intelligence official. Immediately, I left the Palace of Westminster, and appeared in the Russian security supremo's office.

The Russian looked at me. He could see that introductions were not needed. 'Can you give me that too?' he asked.

Now at this point, you might wonder how a Russian security supremo had managed to get access to me in a high security area near the Palace of Westminster. The point was not lost on me, but it was not my problem. That was a matter for the security services, who would know what was happening, as they were monitoring my activities in the building anyway.

From my perspective, the more people that go Green, the

better it is for the planet. So, in answer to the Russian supremo's question, I said, 'Yes. I can give you that too.'

'Please wait a minute,' said the security supremo.

He turned and spoke to two of his staff, who were standing nearby. One of them left the room and returned with a tall soldier in uniform. The soldier saluted respectfully.

'Can you give it to him?' asked the Russian.

I gave the soldier Green energy. He blinked, gave a big smile, and saluted again, while a look of wonder came across his face.

'Let this man have full physical and mental health checks,' said the Russian. 'But first, we need the energy too.'

He called for his secretary to be brought in. She was an elegant, young lady, attractively dressed. This is not unusual for secretaries of senior Russian officials. The Russian asked for the soldier to be brought back, and for him to touch the secretary on the arm. As the soldier appeared, the young lady visibly brightened.

'Hey! What a hunk!' she thought.

'Please touch my secretary on the arm,' said the Russian.

The soldier obeyed, and the secretary's perception of life was transformed. The soldier saluted again and left the room. Then the other officials in the room, and the senior Russian, went and touched the secretary's arm. There was a silence as they began to take in what had happened to them. They could have touched the soldier's arm and got the same result, but perhaps they were too macho for that, or maybe, they were just being cautious.

The Russian thanked me politely, and I left. What has been going on with the Russians since, I do not know, but I hope that the frequency of the Green energy has been passed on to as many people as possible in that country.

US SENATE COMMITTEE

Next day, it was time to visit the senior officials of the US Senate committee, who were now linked into my experience. The first person I made contact with was Frank, the deputy head of the committee. Picking his photo from the committee's internet web page, I tuned into his frequency, and found myself joining a crowd of political aides all hurrying behind a senior man in a smart blue suit, who was on the political campaign trail, visiting a busy shopping centre.

The sun was shining and the Senator was just about to enter a pedestrian precinct, when a band of US mafia terrorists from their Faeces Group decided to attack my bladder. I was wearing shielding underwear, but Frank was not. His bladder released involuntarily and a dark patch appeared on his trousers.

'Oh no, someone has shot me in the butt!' he cried, 'Christ, what can I do?' He dashed into the rest room with his aides.

'Help me, I've got a meeting at 2.00. I must have a change of trousers. Go out and get me some. No, ring my wife. No, there isn't time. Oh Hell!'

Then one of the terrorists decided to aim a blast at my genitals. Really, I wonder why they bother, as it has little effect on me. But it had a big impact on Frank. He fell, gasping in pain.

'I've been shot in the balls! Man, do you have any idea what that feels like?'

Frank's aides hurried off to see if they could get him fresh clothes. While they were gone, I appeared in front of him.

'Hi, I know what just happened to you. The people doing it are from the US Mafia, working with Islamic State, to bring down Western democracies.'

Frank stared at me, as if stunned. It was all a ghastly nightmare to him.

'You need to read my books, *Terror in Britain* and *Kiss Terror Goodbye*,' I told him. Then I disappeared.

With great presence of mind, Frank quickly wrote down the names of my books. Two of his aides came in and he asked them to look up the books on the internet. When they found them, he read the descriptions of the books, and asked his aides to go out and buy them. Other aides appeared, bringing him new trousers.

'I heard this voice telling me about my attackers,' he told them. 'I wonder who I can contact?'

Whispering in his ear, I said, 'Look in my second book for a man called Elliot. He can answer all your questions. He is a military specialist and responsible for ghouls' border controls in New York.'

'What are ghouls?' asked Frank.

'Covert criminals using electromagnetic personas to avoid detection,' I replied. 'You have military and intelligence contacts, ask them to put you in touch with Elliot.'

At this moment, a female member of the Senate committee phoned Frank to tell him she had been targeted with the same attacks as he had. Then Frank received an email from the chairwoman of the committee, addressed to all members, telling them that they were all under targeting attack, and that the matter would be discussed at their next meeting. Committee members were given the name and details of a security official to contact about this.

Immediately, Frank called the number and spoke to the security official. Shortly afterwards, a member of the security services appeared, wearing a dark khaki uniform.

'You are all being targeted,' the man announced calmly, 'but don't worry, we are aware of it and we are monitoring developments closely.'

'Wonderful!' I thought to myself. 'So that's all right then?'

'Do you know of a man called Elliot?' asked Frank.

'Who told you about him?' asked the official cautiously.

'The lady who wrote this book,' said Frank, who now had a copy of *Kiss Terror Goodbye* in his hand. 'I need to talk to him.'

'Ah, yes,' said the official, 'I know who you are referring to. Of course, that's not his real name, though that's the name he goes by. He works in deep space, and cannot be met.'

'What do you mean by deep space?' asked Frank. 'Why wasn't my committee told about this? I have a right to speak to this guy. Go get him.'

Frank spoke with all the authority of a senior Senator. The man left, and Frank started looking for me.

'Hey, Martha, are you there? What is deep space?'

'Oh, hi Frank,' I replied. 'As far as I know, deep space means roughly everything beyond the Earth-Moon area, though definitions keep changing. It may be hard to accept if you haven't been told about it, but the United States has people living on several planets in our galaxy, including Mars. Elliot is involved with all that.'

Frank put his head in his hands and let out a deep sigh. I could tell he was in shock. I decided to help him by sending him Green energy.

'What did you just do?' asked Frank.

'I used an electromagnetic, frequency-raising programme which I wrote, called Green,' I explained. Frank was still coming to terms with what had happened, when Elliot suddenly walked in.

'I hear you wanted to talk to me,' he said.

'Oh, hi. Thanks for coming. Phew... I'm a little overtaken by events. Do you happen to have gone through the Green transformation?' asked Frank.

'I have had that experience,' replied Elliot, 'and she just gave it to the Russians as well.'

'The Russians?' cried Frank, 'I thought she was on our side!'

'She isn't on anyone's side,' said Elliot.

To be fair to Elliot, he did not make it sound like an accusation, just a statement of fact. Elliot turned to Frank.

'We can't talk here, as the whole universe can listen. We need to go across town to a secure installation.'

I took the hint and left at that point. After Frank returned to his office, I looked in again. An officer from Elliot's office, called Martin, was sitting there to provide further advice as required.

The three of us began talking about Elliot's deep space work, and how, owing to decisions on military secrecy, the deep space programme had never been disclosed, even to those responsible for overseeing expenditure on space exploration. Because of this, people had been led to believe that the only way to travel to Mars was by a space vehicle, when in fact it took two seconds, using the "beaming-up" method.

I told Frank how I had recently visited a high frequency planet called Sutor, and I mentioned that my second book describes how astrophysicists from the UK went to Mars in 2017.

'You mean you went there?' said Frank.

'Well, I acted as a courier so that several people could go there,' I explained. Frank frowned and fell silent for a minute. Turning to Martin, he said, 'I think our committee should go there too.'

'That's not possible,' said Martin.

'What gives you the right to deny elected representatives of the people of the United States, the right to check whether tax payers' money has been properly spent on the space programme?' I asked.

'Ah, right,' said Frank. 'That's right. Our committee is entitled to request it.'

'Excuse me a moment,' said Martin, and he left the room, to talk on his cell phone. When Martin returned, his face had lit up.

'It's OK, you can go,' he said, smiling.

Secretly, Martin wanted this to happen, but he just didn't believe it ever would. Now that the project had been given the go ahead, he was quite excited at the prospect of a fact-finding mission of Senators going to Mars.

'I will ring round my committee and see if they want to go and come back to Martha, in four hours,' said Frank.

'Fine,' I thought. 'That will give me time to go back to Howard, the head of the UK parliamentary committee, and update him on developments.'

Howard had set up a temporary office in the basement of the building near the Palace of Westminster. On the advice of the UK military, he had his feet up so that his body was horizontal from the hips down. This prevented terrorists from attacking him with oscillators, which create rocking movements which shake the body when people are standing or walking.

'Hi,' I said, 'I've just visited a representative of the US Senate committee.'

'Oh yes, I know,' replied Howard, giving me a wave as he checked through his paperwork. 'Frank just texted me about that. I like the sound of the higher frequency planet, — any chance of a visit there?'

I had not been expecting this. But I could see no reason why Howard shouldn't go, so I said, 'Give me a few minutes, and I'll be back.'

A moment afterwards, I was outside Don's conservatory. He was inside, busy with white and pink plants that looked like cyclamens. I passed on Howard's request. Don did not want to be discourteous, but you could see that right now, his plants were his highest priority. At that moment, his friend Angus appeared on the side of the conservatory, waving to both of us.

'Give us a hand can you?' said Don, 'Could you see to Martha's query?'

'I'd be delighted,' said Angus.

I explained how Howard was head of a senior UK parliamentary committee, wanting to carry out a fact-finding investigation into interplanetary communications.

'Bring him to the tea room and I'll meet you both there,' said Angus. I returned to Howard. He looked up expectantly.

'You're on,' I said.

'Great, let's go,' said Howard.

I whisked him away and we were soon sitting in the comfortable tea room. Angus came in and shook Howard by the hand.

'Glad to meet you. Would you like to stroll on our new bridge and admire the view?'

Angus and Howard walked along the bridge, and shortly afterwards, Don joined them. The three men strolled, enjoying the invigorating sea breeze and admiring the estuary, with its blue waters lapping against the sides of rolling, green hills. They stood out there for a long time, talking. But Howard began to feel weak. I could see he was suffering from the credibility gap that affects everyone the first time they leave our planet.

'Oh, I'm so sorry, I seem to have come over tired. I'm afraid it's been a bit much for me. I do apologise,' he said to Angus.

'Don't mention it old chap,' said Angus. 'Quite understandable. I know just how you feel. It happened to me, the first time I came here. It's the frequency, a bit higher than we are used to on Earth.'

Howard signalled to me that he would like to return home, and I was just about to take him back, when Angus said, 'Wait — just one minute.'

He returned, carrying a farewell gift. It was a lovely yellow plant in a pot, like a daffodil, with lots of flowers on it. I quickly created a carrier bag for it.

Angus and Don waved goodbye.

'Come back soon!' they called, as Howard and I disappeared.

Then we were back in Howard's room. Howard put the

carrier bag down on the table. Glen, the officer on duty, immediately removed it.

'Hey! That's a gift to me. You can't take it,' said Howard.

'You can't just bring things back to Earth,' said Glen. 'It will have to go for investigation.'

'Never mind, Howard,' I said, 'I'll make a copy of it for you,' and I did.

Howard was just beginning to get his breath back and recover from his high frequency experience, when a scientist in a white lab coat appeared.

'Are you the gentleman who brought back the plant?' he asked Howard. 'The results of our initial tests are most exciting, most exciting!'

'Oh good,' said Howard, without much interest. He started to go through his papers again.

'Wait, what is that?' said the scientist, eyeing up the replacement plant. 'Oh, I just made a copy, since the original had been removed,' I explained.

The scientist put on his glasses.

'That will be very useful for comparison purposes,' he said. He picked up the pot, and walked off with it.

'Oh, take it for goodness' sake,' said Howard.

By now he was quite irritated by this white-coated figure.

Howard was beginning to wilt again. It was the shock of space travel. He loved meeting Angus and Don, but right now, his mind and body were reeling. I created a magick food table and produced an energy drink for him, after which he began to feel better.

'What's that you just did?' asked Glen, 'It looks interesting.'

'Here, try this,' I replied, making him another. 'You just

look at the table and think what you want to eat or drink, and it appears.'

In a matter of minutes, several other officials had joined him. 'Best I ever tasted,' said Glen, sipping his beer.

'What will happen if Glen's boss appears?' I thought.

If Glen's boss had appeared, I was ready to explain that Glen was not drinking alcohol on duty. It was just a high frequency vitamin and mineral drink. But if Glen's boss was one of the men gathered round the table, he certainly wasn't saying anything.

Then Howard got a text from Frank, asking how he got on with his planet trip. Frank also reported that he couldn't get the rest of the US group to agree about the Mars trip, because of difficulties with travel insurance. Howard was just reading this out, when Glen came over.

'I'm sorry, Sir, but you're not really supposed to use the phone for text messages,' he said. 'It's for security reasons.'

'Right,' I thought, 'We'll see about that,' and I went straight over to Frank's office, where he was relaxing on the sofa, attended by a US duty officer.

'Hi, Frank, the UK military say Howard shouldn't text you for security reasons. Would you like to come over and chat with him instead?'

'Yes, Martha, let's go now!' said Frank.

As we left, the US duty officer put his head in his hands. A minute later, Frank was sitting next to Howard on his leather sofa. Both men decided to try wine from the magick restaurant table, and Frank created a fancy sea-food dish. Then Frank and Howard took joint selfies and emailed them to all the members of their two groups. I left them chatting about their experiences.

There were things to be done. It was over a year since I had been in touch with officers at the Mars base, and I needed to update them on the planned visit. But I knew they had their own methods of keeping tabs on what was going on down here.

I presented myself respectfully at the front entrance to the Mars base. As I arrived, I was surprised to find that it now had an imposing gate, a driveway and a staircase leading up to a veranda on the

first floor, where the main door was now located. What a change from the underground portal I had been used to before.

'How do they keep this from showing up on photographs from Earth?' I thought.

Ed, the head of the Mars base, a tall, mature man in a dark suit, came out onto the veranda. 'Martha! How nice to see you again! I think I know why you have come. Is it about the American Senate committee visit?'

'Yes. It is,' I said.

'Please tell them they are most welcome,' said Ed. 'We just need a formal request from the US Military, but that should be no problem.'

'Great,' I said. 'When is it convenient for the delegation to arrive?'

'Any time,' said Ed. 'We are always open here, and you may have noticed, our hospitality unit has been expanded to take larger groups.'

'OK. I'll get back to the Senate committee, and hope to see you soon,' I replied.

It was now time for me to go back to Westminster, to pick up Frank and take him back to his office. I reappeared in Howard's basement room, and he and Frank said their goodbyes.

'Are you ready to go, Frank?' I said.

'Yes,' said Frank, 'fire away.'

As we left, Glen, the UK duty officer stepped forward. 'Actually, Martha, there's no need for you to do that. We can do it.'

In fact, the UK military could have done it anytime, but they never offered to, before. I guess they decided it was better to keep control of the situation rather than have their VIPs flying about unguarded. But their offer was too late, as Frank and I were already back in the US, in his office.

FIRST MARS VISIT

The US military had arranged for all members of the Senate committee, now linked to my targeting experience, to have offices in the same building. That way, they could work together while being given full security protection. I went to meet the head of the committee, a sharp-minded lady called Linda, and I offered all members of the committee the Green energy. There was a pause while the committee started to see things from a wider perspective.

'Hey, does that mean I can create things?' asked Linda.

'Provided the electromagnetic environment is suitable, you can create anything,' I replied.

'Great!' laughed Linda, 'I could do with a new outfit.'

She playfully tested out her new abilities. Some of the men gave themselves Rolex watches, just to see if they could. They laughed when they realised how easy it is to create things from mind.

'To think we could solve so many world problems, like illness and poverty, and the military did not want to share the technology with us,' said Linda.

'Hey guys, did you all get the pictures of me and Howard today?' asked Frank. 'Half an hour ago, I was in London with the head of their parliamentary committee, enjoying the best meal I ever tasted, and in less than a minute, I was back here. Think how things could change if we all started doing that. The other committee members applauded, as Frank continued, 'Howard was gracious enough to share with me how today he went on a visit to a high frequency planet called Sutor, where he was made to feel right at home by two Scottish gentlemen. Imagine that. He was there and back in less than two hours. And think, Ladies and Gentlemen, what that could mean for travel to Mars.'

Members of the committee cheered at this. They were clearly raring to go on their own planetary exploration. It was time to get into the detail of the arrangements.

'There are two things to know about going to Mars,' I said. 'The first is, Mars has gone Green at subatomic particle level, and all people on Mars have received Green energy. They now insist that anyone visiting them must have Green energy as well. Of course, you all qualify on that basis. The other requirement is that you must have an invitation from the Mars authorities to go up there. I have already checked with them that they would be delighted to welcome you, but you need to make a formal request through your military.'

Linda turned to the duty officer standing at the back of the room. 'Marcus, can that be arranged, please?'

'Just give me a moment, Linda,' said Marcus, looking worried.

He knew that the whole idea of going to Mars was highly irregular, but he also knew that a decision had been taken at the highest level not to antagonise the Senate committee. It was not long before he returned.

'It's been agreed. Please can your committee be here tomorrow at 2 p.m., and we'll take it from there?'

Everyone cheered, and went off to their rooms to get on with their work. In the back of my mind, I could hear Howard's voice. He had been listening to everything, via the terrorists' ultrasound system, which connected all people linked into my experience.

'I want to go to Mars. Why wasn't my committee given the chance?' Howard muttered to himself. Immediately, I reappeared in his room.

'Of course, you can go. Do you want all your committee to go?'

Howard went off to consult them, and naturally, they all wanted the opportunity. I asked the UK military to check if the Mars base could handle two groups at once, and if the Senate committee were happy to go at the same time as the British one. The answer was yes to both questions, so I agreed to collect both groups at 2 p.m. the next day.

That night, I and all the committee members in the US, UK and Europe were attacked by the terrorists, using bladder voiding technology and a combination of oscillators and stomach cramp targeting effects. It was distressing for the committee delegates, and a chilling reminder of the criminal abuse of specialist technologies going on, unchecked on Earth. The terrorists were frustrated at the way the focus constantly moved away from them, and they tried to make their presence felt in the usual ways. However, their attacks had no impact at all outside the Earth's magnetic field. So the trips to Mars would be a respite for all the delegates.

Next day, at 1.30 p.m., I checked in on both the UK and US groups to make sure they were ready, and to let them know I hadn't forgotten them. It was cold in London, and the UK group were wearing coats, scarfs, woolly socks and boots, because they thought it would be cold on Mars. I took the opportunity to offer them all Green energy, and all the UK military officers on duty asked to be included as well.

The US group were more 'ready to roll' than their UK counterparts. They were in great spirits and had been doing their homework on targeted individuals. Linda asked me a lot of questions about Islamic State, IRA terrorists and Mafia collaboration. The US delegates could hear terrorists making rude comments about them via the ultrasound system that linked in to me.

'What do you do about that, Martha?' asked a lady delegate.

'Just take no notice,' I replied. 'If it bothers you, put on music or listen to the radio. That drowns them out.'

'When can we go?' said another delegate, 'I'm ready now.'

'Yes, we're all ready!' shouted the others.

I got a message from the Mars base, saying that if the US group were ready, they could come now. Then I got a call from the UK group. A lady called Angela was worried about further bladder attacks by the terrorists and wanted to leave right away to escape. I created protective underwear for her, and issued personalised packs to all the delegates in both groups, to reassure them. Linda took pity on Angela.

'I say we let the UK group go first,' she announced. 'Can I have a show of hands?'

The US group kindly agreed to let the Brits go first. So I went back to London to get them. They weren't quite ready, and scurried around getting their things together. Then they gathered in their lounge. Howard did a headcount to check they were all there. Then he gave me the go ahead. I picked them all up and deposited them inside the gates of the Mars base, where they were able to breath without helmets.

Ed came out onto the veranda to welcome them. Seeing their winter clothes, he said, 'Hey, you won't need all that gear. It's a baking eighty degrees Fahrenheit in here. Would you like to leave your outer clothes in the foyer? You can collect them on your way out.'

While the UK group were doing that, I went back to get the US group. Despite their enthusiasm, they were not quite ready either, and Frank hadn't arrived yet, as he thought they were still leaving at 2 p.m., which was ten minutes away.

'Give us another ten minutes,' said Linda.

I went back to the Mars base to let them know there would be a slight delay. Ed went in to talk to the hospitality technical team.

'We can't keep the air-lock on for ten minutes,' said a technician, 'We'll have to turn it off and turn it on again.'

Just then I heard Linda's voice calling, 'We're ready, Martha.'

'It's OK, they're just coming,' I told Ed.

I whizzed back to the US committee lounge. The delegates were all grouped together, so I picked them up and set them down in front of the veranda. Then I heard a call. 'Wait for me!'

It was Frank. I raced back.

'It's OK, Frank, you're not too late,' I reassured him.

Frank's secretary came running in with some papers. 'Don't forget your speech. Here it is.'

Frank grabbed the papers.

'I'm ready!' he gasped, and I whisked him away.

As Frank arrived, the last of the US delegates was being ushered in. I took a quick look through the doors of the Mars base. I could see light coming in through huge windows on the other side, and everyone crowding round to have a look. Then Ed whispered to me, 'It's OK Martha, you can come in too.'

'Wowee!' I thought.

My eyes welled up for a moment, at the thought that I was to be included. Then my excitement overcame my emotion. I couldn't wait to go in. I left the foyer and entered a huge viewing room with enormous windows, giving a panoramic vista across the planet. The delegates were all crowding round to look out.

The scene was breathtaking. A vast desert of red sand was outside, with paler dunes in the background, under a hazy pink sky. You felt as if you were out there. In the distance, grey-blue hills framed the incredible landscape. On the right-hand side of the viewing area, there were dark, rocky hills jutting out. The scene was starkly beautiful, with the light of our sun filtering through.

Next to the viewing room, up a set of wooden stairs, was a bar and drinks area, with another viewing window. It seemed strange that this building could be on the surface of Mars, and yet invisible from Earth. I would have looked into this further, but Ed asked me not to reveal how it is done. Then I checked up on the delegates. First, I looked for Frank.

'Do you need anything, Frank?' I asked. 'You had to leave in such a rush.'

'Oh, I'm fine,' said Frank. 'Actually, can you bring my briefcase, if possible?'

'Sure,' I said.

It only took a moment to retrieve the briefcase.

'In fact,' I explained, 'you all have the ability to do this yourself.'

'Do we?' asked Linda.

'Yes,' I said.

'In that case...' said Linda, and she re-created her make-up bag, which she had left behind in the US Senate lounge.

Most of the delegates were admiring the view, but I noticed that Howard and Angela were sitting down, looking tired.

'What's wrong? Are you all right?' I asked.

'Angela is feeling unwell,' said Howard, 'and I'm not feeling too good myself.'

I sent them both an energy beam, which made them feel better. I made Angela an energy drink, and was about to offer it to her, when the bar-tender, whose name was Eric, came running over.

'I'm afraid you can't do that here,' he said, 'All drinks have to come from the bar.'

He pointed to an overhead rack, from which many bottles were suspended, with taps like those in modern pubs. I explained that Angela wasn't feeling well.

'But I'm feeling much better now,' said Angela.

'The thing is,' said Eric, 'liquids can be difficult to absorb up here, if they haven't been specially treated.'

Another UK lady was looking sea sick. Ed came out from behind the bar. 'Anybody feeling unwell?' he asked.

Several people put up their hands. Ed handed out packets of tablets to everyone and they soon felt better.

I left them to it, and went back to my garden to plant bulbs. I was not due to collect the delegates for four hours, and I had lots to do. But I was happy that elected representatives of two countries were finally getting in on the secret space programme.

After three hours, I checked back. The delegates were

sitting in the bar area, around three tables, all talking avidly to each other. Ed asked me if I would make magick restaurant tables for the Mars astronauts. I made a few, and men who had been working outside the base came into the bar to receive their personal tables. They went and sat at the back of the bar area, eating piles of orange-brown bite-size things. They were picking up bits and dropping them into their mouths, with great enjoyment.

'What are you eating?' I asked one of them.

'Scampi,' the man replied.

Turns out this is their favourite food, and they can't get it on Mars. Ed came over.

'I'm sorry Martha, we're running late. Could you pick the delegates up two hours later than we planned?'

'Sure,' I said.

I noticed that it had gone dark outside.

'Is it night outside?' I asked.

'No,' said Ed, 'we have covered the windows for security reasons.'

He would not be drawn further on this, but afterwards, when I was sitting quietly at home, I received information directly into my mind, explaining that astronauts were outside completing tasks on the Mars surface. These tasks, which were part of the Mars base's normal objectives, were highly classified, and too sensitive to be discussed.

Since there was going to be a delay, I decided to visit members of a French parliamentary committee, who were also getting targeted whenever I was. When I arrived, they were sitting round a table talking to their military duty officer.

'Why won't you tell us what has happened?' asked a lady. 'We cannot contact either the US or UK groups. Both of them have disappeared. You must know what is going on.'

'I'm sorry, Madame,' said the duty officer, 'I cannot tell you anything.'

'Who gives you the authority to say that?' she asked, 'Is it the French government?'

'No,' replied the duty officer.

'You have no right to refuse us information. Who are you taking orders from? Are you above the French government?'

The duty officer turned and looked at me. He had been aware of my presence all the time. 'Can you help me out?' he said. 'I have to obey orders. I want them to have the information, but only you can give it to them.'

I made myself visible. The duty officer pointed to me. 'She can answer your questions.'

I introduced myself, and explained, 'The US and UK delegates have gone to visit a Mars base on a fact-finding mission, which will take all day.'

There was much excitement among the French delegates. 'I knew it!' said one man.

'We heard rumours from other groups,' said another.

'I expect the US and UK delegates texted them,' I thought.

'If you want to get an idea about the Mars visit, there is a chapter in *Kiss Terror Goodbye*, which describes it,' I said.

The head of the French committee turned to the duty officer. 'Please can you get us copies of this book?'

The duty officer left the room and returned immediately with several copies. They must have been created using thought. That indicated the level of clearance the French security services were operating at.

'Well, if we have got that far,' I thought, 'I might as well give them everything the other groups have got.'

So I explained about Green energy, and the French delegates and their military duty officers, all said they would like to receive it. Then I created magick restaurant tables for them. I was not sure how the French would receive this, with their renowned gourmet expertise and refined tastes.

'Let the tables look how the French would like them to,' I said.

The tables came out looking like nineteenth century mahogany coffee tables. I explained how they were used. Two of the men created a bottle of red wine. They did not drink immediately, but started commenting on the 'bouquet.' I noticed a lady tasting the food, but not eating it, because she wanted to stay slim.

'No need to worry about bad effects from this food,' I announced, 'It will not put on weight, make you drunk or give you a hangover, because it is made from pure high-frequency components.'

It was time to go back to the Mars base, and I left the French delegates, enjoying their meal. When I arrived, the British group were already in the foyer, putting on their winter clothes. Their average age was somewhat higher than that of the Americans, and they looked tired.

'I think we had better let the Brits go first,' said Linda, the US Senate committee head.

It was dark now, and technicians switched the lights on outside. Descending from the veranda, Angela lost her footing. I caught her, and two men helped her to join the others. The group assembled outside the base. Howard did a head count, and thanked Ed for his hospitality. Then he waved to me to take them back.

Next minute, they were in their basement lounge near the

Palace of Westminster. They all fell back on chairs and sofas, relieved it was over. Space travel and space visits can be stressful, if you're not used to them. Then all the UK delegates retired to their rooms and settled down with their smartphones.

I went back to Mars. After Angela slipped, it was decided that the Americans should not go down the staircase. They were led out by a fire exit. As they gathered together outside, Frank read out his speech. Linda formally thanked Ed, and waved goodbye to the men lined up on the veranda to see them off. I picked them up and returned them to their communal lounge. As they arrived, they let out whistles and cheers. Then they all began to talk and laugh, getting rid of any tension from the transfer.

I went back to the French group, to let them know that the US and UK groups had returned. But the room was dark and empty. The French had already found out that they were back, and were on the phone to the space travellers, and to their friends all over Europe.

IGRASHEL AND ARTURUS GO GREEN

Next day, Howard was sitting in his basement room, with his feet up on a stool and a rug over his legs, having a coffee and reading his emails. His duty officer was in attendance when I went to visit him.

'Oh, hello Martha,' he said, 'I've been thinking. It would be good if at least one representative from each EU country could have a space visit. Perhaps it should be more than one representative, as if you want them to lobby for disclosure of information in their own countries, they will need moral support.'

'Good idea,' I said. 'To spread the hospitality load, there are plenty of other planets with American colonies. Perhaps we should think of visiting them.'

I had in mind visits to Arturus and Igrashel, but those planets had not gone Green yet and would need to, before receiving delegations from Earth. At that moment, Ed, the head of the Mars base, appeared on my mental screen.

'We could do one more visit like the one we did yesterday,' he said. 'But it would be good if other planets could be involved in hosting visits as well.'

I remembered a conversation that I'd had with Ed the day before, while on Mars. Ed told me that visitors to Mars from Arturus caused a lot of trouble by not complying with interplanetary agreements. He also said that the Arturus authorities permitted an environment like the Wild West to operate on their planet. Ed had said he thought Arturus ought to go Green as a priority.

'Ooh! going to other planets!' said Howard. His face lit up. 'If we're going to new planets, I hope the US and UK can go.'

'Of course, they can,' I said. 'Now, I'd better go and find out which planets would be willing to host fact-finding visits.'

I started by landing on planet Igrashel, outside the glass city I had seen before. The sun streamed across, brightening the blue sky. I looked for a Parliament building, but could only find a Court of Law, with barristers in black gowns and wigs. It seemed out of date for such a modern city. I tuned into the universal computer.

'Where can I find the person in charge here?' I asked.

My gaze was directed to the top of a glass skyscraper. Making myself invisible, I headed straight up there, and arrived in a large office, with panoramic views, like a penthouse. A fit-looking man in his early forties, called Dominic, wearing a classic navy suit, was talking to his secretary. The young lady was in her twenties, wearing a "New Look" dress, with a balloon skirt and tiny waist. Her short brown hair was in a style straight out of the 1950s.

'I must go now,' he said. 'I'm just popping in here.'

He dashed to the rest room, and came out drying his hands on a towel. 'I'll see you tomorrow,' he said, pressing the call button for the lift.

'Very good, Sir,' replied his secretary.

Dominic got into the lift, and I followed, still invisible. On the way down, he started adjusting his hair. It had been a busy morning, and he hadn't had time to check his image. As he looked in the mirror, I materialised behind him.

'Aagh!' Dominic let out a cry of shock.

I guess I should have waited 'til he got out of the lift.

'It's all right,' I said. 'No need to worry. You're perfectly safe.'

'Are you that Martha person?' Dominic asked.

'Yes,' I said.

'Oh good. I've just been hearing about you. Look, give me a few minutes and we can talk.'

Dominic hurried out of the building, where a car was waiting for him. There were three junior staff in the back, two women and a man, all smartly dressed in office suits.

'I'm afraid I'm going to have to drop you off at the airport,' Dominic said as he got in the car.

He got into the front passenger seat. At first, I had the impression there was someone sitting in the driver's seat, but then I realised there was no one there. In spite of that, the car started up and drove off, and Dominic began talking to the invisible driver. The steering wheel turned as if someone's hand was guiding it. It was his private secretary, sitting at a desk in an office, taking note of what he was saying, and directing the car remotely.

The car pulled in to a parking space outside a small airport, and the three staff got out. 'That's better,' Dominic said to his invisible assistant.

He turned to me.

'Do have a seat. I'm Dominic. Nice to meet you.' He held out his hand.

'Are you the head of this planet?' I asked.

'No,' said Dominic, 'I'm the deputy. The head of our

planet left just before you arrived. But we're going to catch up with him.'

The car sped off, and pulled in outside some buildings. Dominic got out and went into the building. He was back almost immediately.

'Too late,' he said, 'We've missed him.'

'Is he in an aircraft?' I asked.

'No,' said Dominic, 'he just took off by himself in that direction.' Dominic pointed to the sky.

'I can still catch up with him,' I said, 'if you think of a picture of him in your head for a moment.'

'OK,' said Dominic, and I got the image.

A moment later, we were in the back of a large limousine, going fast across the desert, but very smoothly. We were about twenty-five feet above the ground, leaving a white con trail behind us. *11. The sky was a pinky-brown colour, and the beige desert sand spread out below us.

The man in the front seat was Stephan, the head of Planet Igrashel. He looked about fifty years old, medium build, with short dark hair, greying slightly over his forehead. He already knew we were coming, as Dominic's private secretary had told Stephan's private secretary, who though not present, was piloting the airborne car.

'Stephan, this is Martha,' said Dominic.

'Nice to meet you,' said Stephan, smiling, 'I understand that you are interested in arranging for a delegation from Earth to visit our planet.'

'Yes,' I said.

'That would be fine,' said Stephan. We could take up to three groups of thirty people on three different days. But at this stage, that's unofficial. We have to go through the proper channels.'

'Thank you, that's great,' I said. 'Can I pass that on, unofficially, to delegate representatives on Earth?'

'Yes,' said Stephan, 'but don't quote me 'til it's official.'

'There is something else,' I said. 'The Mars base and the entire Mars planet have had a frequency transformation.'

'Oh yes,' said Dominic, 'I heard about that.'

That confirmed my suspicion that he had been talking to the Mars base.

'I was going to ask,' I continued, 'whether you would be interested in having your planet go the same way?'

Both men gave me their full attention. 'Yes please, Martha,' said Stephan.

Immediately, I selected both men, and sent them the Green energy.

Dominic sat back in his seat with a gasp. Stephan suddenly laughed with surprise and elation. Then he said, 'I expect you would like to stop for a minute to fix the planet.'

'Yes,' I said, and I left.

Landing on the flat, sandy desert below, I selected the planet at subatomic particle level, and turned it Green. Then I returned to the flying vehicle. The two men were already discussing logistics for the fact-finding visits from Earth. When I reappeared, Dominic produced a yellow flower in a brown, ceramic pot.

'Look,' said Dominic proudly, 'I made it myself.'

'Oh, you've worked out how to create from mind already,' I said.

'We do have your book here,' said Stephan, 'so we were only waiting for the opportunity.'

At that moment, the vehicle landed on the desert floor,

outside a large, clay, brick building. Half way up, the building had glass walls and a glass roof.

'I'd like to stop here,' said Stephan, 'to check what impact the transformation has had on people.' He and Dominic got out, and I followed. Several staff members came out of the building towards him.

'Well, did you feel anything?' Dominic asked.

'Oh yes, I feel much brighter!' said one woman. 'Our team guessed immediately, and they've already started making things.'

Several young people in their twenties came running out. One had a yellow flower in a pot, identical to the one Dominic had made.

'Look,' she said, coming up to me, 'it's our country's national symbol.'

'It's a pretty plant,' I said, admiring its yellow flower.

'Yes,' said the young woman, 'we've got lots like this growing on our sun roof.'

I looked up and saw a fresh green garden with a lot of ferns and palms under the glass roof on the top floor. A young man stepped forward holding a magick restaurant table.

'We've just made this,' he said, 'and it works!' Then Dominic asked me, 'Would you mind signing a few copies of your book?'

I realised that this was a diplomatic set up, and that the surprise stop-off in the desert had been planned as a courtesy to me. I selected the books the young people were holding, and signed them all at the same time. The manifestations created by his staff were sufficient evidence to convince Stephan that Igrashel had indeed gone Green. We got back in the car, and I asked, 'Do you have a Parliamentary system, or how are countries on your planet governed?'

'No, we don't have such a system,' replied Stephan. 'We all report to a central governing committee, which is chaired by planet Arturus.'

'How did that system develop?' I asked.

'Well,' said Stephan, 'originally, it was like countries on Earth in the old British Empire, now called Commonwealth countries, I believe.'

'Yes,' I said, feeling embarrassed at the reference to our old Empire.

'You see,' said Stephan, 'at first, all the planets were part of a group identity. Then, over time, they got their independence.'

'But Commonwealth countries on Earth all have Parliamentary democracies,' I pointed out.

'I know,' said Stephan. 'It's an issue we need to resolve, but the problem is getting all the other planets in the group to agree, particularly Arturus.'

'How would it be,' I asked, 'if I were to contact Arturus and the other planets in the group, and see what can be done?'

'That would be good,' said Stephan.

'Well,' I said, 'I was planning to visit Arturus after meeting you, anyway. So I will take it from there.'

And that's how we left it. Stephan thought I meant to visit planet Arturus immediately, but it was not 'til next morning, that I decided to pay a discrete visit, to find out what was going on there. Making myself invisible, I tuned into where decisions were being taken. It was a large, plain room, with beige walls, conference facilities, and a refreshment area at one end. Five men were sitting round a small, polished-wood table, drinking cappuccinos.

'I thought I saw her arrive just then,' said a man called Erith, who seemed to be the head of Arturus.

'I didn't see anything,' said the man opposite him.

'Well,' said Erith, 'if she doesn't arrive soon we'll have to leave, because there isn't anything more we can do on our own.'

It was obvious that they had been waiting for me. I decided to make myself visible. 'Ah, there she is,' said Erith, 'Hi Martha, would you like to join us?'

I went and sat at the table.

'We have come to a decision that we want to go forward with the upgrade proposal. Would you like to assist us?'

'Sure,' I said, 'I'll do it right now.'

I stood up and selected the planet at subatomic particle level, and made it go Green. Then I sat down again. The men round the table and waitresses standing in the background all brightened up. They looked around, as if reassessing their view of the world.

'Well, I must admit, that is a lot better,' one of the men whispered to his colleagues around the table.

'How many of you are from other planets?' I asked.

Two of the men put up their hands, and gave the names of the planets they represented, which I did not recognise. One of them said to Erith, 'Actually, would it be all right if I go now, as I need to get back to my own place? I think I understand what I need to do to get the upgrade.'

'You can always give me a call if you need help,' I added.

'Yes, can you arrange for me to go too?' said the other visitor.

Officials came in and escorted the two planetary representatives to the "beaming-up" room. Once they had gone, three white angels with yellow hair, pale gold wings, and long, green robes appeared, floating along the ceiling. Erith looked up at them, smiling.

'Don't worry,' said the first angel, 'everything's going to be all right. We are here to help you now.'

'Ah,' said Erith, 'We were hoping to see you…'

I slipped quietly away. I could see that the leaders of Arturus were going to be busy for a while.

JOURNALISTS PICK UP THE SCENT

Back home, the terrorists were lining up for some attacks. Now that so many important people got targeted whenever I did, they regarded this as an expansion of their empire. But they couldn't do anything until I appeared. As soon as I came into view, I heard a voice say, 'All right men, now let's get some harassing done.'

I could see a black-hatted villain standing on a rock, directing operations. 'Do you mean hazing?' piped up a small terrorist.

'Don't you mean fazing?' squeaked an even smaller terrorist. *12

Up 'til then, they hadn't noticed that their handlers had given them miniature status. They were all of two inches high. Reading my thoughts, another one shouted, 'She's got it wrong! I'm sure I'm three inches high.'

'Yes, so am I,' wittered a fourth voice.

My mind turned to the well-known verse:

"Said the mouse to the elephant, 'aren't you big?' Said the elephant, 'aren't you small?'

Said the mouse to the elephant, 'Yes, I know, I've not been well, at all'."

At that, a few of the ghouls started giggling. I do not tolerate giggling on the battlefield. If terrorists are not 'combat-ready,' then as far as I am concerned, they count as civilians, who should not be there, and need to be handed over to the US military.

'All gigglers in existence, go Green,' I announced, sending them off to the US New York portal. One of the ruffians activated a laser beam, targeted to void my bladder. As I wear a shielding

device, I took no notice. The villain leapt from his post with a satisfied look.

'This is good,' he said. 'I can press the button. It doesn't affect her, so I won't get hit back. Also, I can get all those posh people linked to her, to wet their pants. And now that I've done my duty, I can send myself to the United States and be free.'

He looked up at his managers, who were sitting at what they thought was a safe distance on the balcony above.

'Can I go now?' he asked.

'If you must,' came the reply.

They had to agree, as that was part of the deal. But they had hoped to get me to kill him, for which they would have been awarded a credit point by their bosses. With complete confidence, the ruffian bawled out, 'I want to go to the United States!'

Next minute, he arrived at the entrance to the US military ghouls' immigration portal, where he was directed to the 'tradesman's entrance,' reserved for people taken into custody. The US military supervise the activities of these ghouls twenty-four seven. Although their terms of engagement do not permit

them to intervene, they know exactly who did what to who, and when the villains arrive, they know how to deal with them.

It was time for me to go and check on the EU Security and Defence committee, as I had not yet made contact with them. When I arrived, their Brussels office was empty, except for a few parliamentary researchers. One of them, a young woman, was on the phone.

'There's nobody there. They've all been told to stay at home because of the attacks. No, I don't know when they are coming back.'

Just then, a military intelligence officer wearing protective clothing appeared. He was talking on his cell phone:

'What? Say, again, I didn't catch that… Their bowels and bladders have been attacked and they're not happy about it. Well, I can understand that. At least they are at home. No, they can't come in. We've had feedback from the US Senate committee that it is insensitive to expect them to come in. Seems that the Americans felt demeaned by being herded together and forced to witness each other running to the rest room and emerging with wet clothes.'

'Hmm. Doesn't sound as if there's going to be any action here for a while,' I thought.

I noticed two young women, Claire and Laura, standing nearby. At first, I thought they were research assistants. Then I spotted their notebooks. They were journalists looking for a story. Claire went over to the intelligence officer. 'Excuse me, is it true that the Security and Defence committee are being kept in isolation? Can you tell me why this is happening?'

'No Ma'am, I can't,' the officer replied.

'I heard that they are being targeted with malicious electronic weapon attacks,' said Laura.

'Who told you that?' asked the officer.

'A member of the French Parliamentary Defence

committee,' Laura replied.

'I gather that this sort of thing used to happen before in Germany, when the Americans were first stationed there,' said Claire. 'But it was all hushed up. I'm going to talk to the German delegates about it.'

She walked towards the door leading to the bar used by delegates of EU committees. 'No! You can't!' said the officer.

He stood in front of the door, blocking the way.

'I can't allow this. You don't understand. These matters are classified.' The two women turned on him.

'You've got no right to stop me!' shouted Claire.

'So now we see who's suppressing information,' shouted Laura. 'It's the military as usual. You can't stop us.'

The officer stood his ground, but two of his colleagues came running over.

'Leon, you can't do this. They have the right... let them through.'

As Leon's resolve began to weaken, Claire pushed past him and left. She headed straight for a bar where a lot of German parliamentarians were relaxing. Two men were leaning against the counter.

'Hi,' said Claire, 'have you heard, the EU Security and Defence committee have been put in isolation because they are being targeted with electronic attacks.'

One of the men looked at her in surprise, the other shrugged his shoulders. 'We've heard this before. We are used to it. It is nothing, just a few weirdos. I take no notice of these things. It doesn't affect me.'

Laura slipped into the bar and joined Claire. Then she turned to another man. 'So you know about these attacks? They've happened before?'

At that moment, a man further down the bar, who had been listening, waved at her. 'Come over here, I can tell you more about this.'

He pointed to a nearby table. The two women joined him.

'You know, when the US Military were first stationed here, we had cases of this. But it was kept under wraps.'

'What was happening?' asked Laura.

'There were people targeting individuals, using technologies taken from clinical applications, to make them void the bladder and bowel involuntarily. They were demanding protection money. People were paying them, but it was never enough. The criminals used to take the money and ask for more, and if they didn't get it, they started attacking again.'

'Oh,' said Claire, 'demanding money with menaces. It's an old crime, with a technological twist.'

As the two women took notes, I heard a group of old ghouls behind me crowding together, listening and gloating in coarse raucous voices. 'We used to do a lot more than that in the old days.'

'Oh, yes, we used to target young women, pretty ones. Had them on their knees, sobbing and begging us to stop.'

'Made them give us sex, then targeted them again.'

'They couldn't go to the cops, 'cos no one believed them. I mean, where's the evidence?'

I was fairly sickened by this, but I had heard it all before. I was preoccupied with something else. I was worried that the two planetary representatives I had met on Arturus would not be able to turn their planets Green. So rather than listen to ghoulish talk, I went to check on that.

When I arrived, I found that neither representative had

managed to turn their planets Green. I fixed the first planet and moved onto the second. I was curious to know what, if anything, would happen after the second planet went Green, so I stood in a thicket of shrubs by a main road to see what

was going on. As I watched, two trucks pulled into the side of the road. The drivers got out smiling, and shook hands, congratulating each other. They had obviously been told what going Green would do for them.

One of the men looked at his truck and turned it into the shiniest, smartest lorry you have ever seen. We don't have lorries as big as that on Earth. The other man took a look at the shining beast, and in a few seconds, he had one too. Then they both waved to each other, got into their chariots and drove off. So now the entire Arturus planetary group had gone Green. People on those planets would never again suffer from poverty, illness or old age.

Next day, I returned to the EU Security and Defence committee room. This time, the committee members were back at their desks. I introduced myself to the committee head, who welcomed me warmly, saying he hoped I could organise a trip to Mars. Before I could respond to his request, Ed, the head of the Mars base, appeared in my mind's eye.

'Hi Martha, it's OK, we can take them. In fact, we can take them in a few minutes, and we can arrange for their return as well. By the way, please could you tell the delegates that the temperature inside the Mars base today is seventy degrees Fahrenheit?'

On hearing the news, the committee members rushed around getting coats and hats, even though they had been told it would be seventy degrees up there. Then a senior military official came in.

'OK everyone, please get ready. We will be taking you up to the Mars base.'

'Amazing!' I thought. 'This will establish a new precedent, if I don't have to do it.'

One or two of the delegates, who had been briefed by their French counterparts, looked worried. 'Are you sure it will be safe?' asked one woman. 'I thought Martha would do it.'

The military official assured them that it was perfectly safe. All the delegates had to do was to climb up a set of steps into a transparent, cylindrical, beaming-up device, and next minute, they were on Mars.

I followed after them. They were already on the first floor of the Mars base, excitedly running towards the windows. I was about to send them all Green energy, as I had done for other groups of delegates, but Ed raised his hand, signalling me to stop.

'Wait a minute, Martha,' he said. 'We'd like to test our theory that anyone arriving on a planet that has gone Green gets the same energy.'

After a few minutes, Ed confirmed that everyone had received the upgrade. And that was it! I didn't have to supervise, or act as a courier. The European Union and American military organised the whole thing. This represented a significant change of policy, and a willingness on behalf of the military to engage with politicians about the existence of an advanced space programme.

Later that day, I checked in on the EU committee common room. The delegates had just returned from Mars, and were getting their belongings together before going home. They looked tired but focused, as if united by a common purpose to fulfil their responsibilities as democratically elected representatives.

Their job now would be to report to the appropriate forum within the EU Parliament about their fact-finding visit. Unfortunately, the appropriate forum was bound to be highly classified, making it unlikely that the committee's report would be available to the public.

Outside in the car park, the two women reporters were sitting in their black Renault Clio, back on the case. Laura was on the phone to her boss.

'Still no movement. They've been there all day. The place is cordoned off... I can't get through... No, wait, something's happening. They're coming out. Hey, what's this? I don't believe it. Looks like they've got a full military escort.'

'Stay with it, Laura,' her boss's voice came over the phone. 'Sounds like something big is going on. Whatever it takes, I want this story. See if you can get interviews, or why not try your French contacts? Keep up the good work now. Byee.'

Laura smiled, closing her phone. She turned to Claire. 'Seems he's still willing to pay us, anyway.'

'What next?' asked Claire.

'What next?' replied Laura. 'I need to make a phone call. If I play my cards right, we could be eating out in France this evening.'

That evening, I checked back on the intrepid pair. They were sitting in a café on the French side of the border. Outside, Antoine, a man with dark hair, in his fifties, was preparing to make a discreet entrance. He turned up the collar of his jacket as he slipped in through a side door. His eyes searched the crowded room, then he saw a female hand waving in his direction.

'We're over here, Antoine!' shouted Claire, blowing his cover.

'So much for my discretion,' thought Antoine.

The two young women stood and extended their cheeks, for the customary continental embrace. Then, as the waiter pushed his way through the mass of wooden chairs, Laura said:

'Well, Antoine, what is it to be, an espresso, or do we have something to celebrate tonight?'

'Laura,' said Antoine, shrugging his shoulders, 'you know me. Would I disappoint a lady?'

'Oh good,' said Claire. 'Suddenly I feel a party coming on. A bottle of red wine, please, Monsieur,' she called out to the waiter. 'Antoine, would you like to choose? The boss is paying.'

'Ah, mes amis,' said Antoine, 'I wish you had been with us a few days ago. What wine we had then. Now that was a real party!'

'Oh, do tell,' said Laura encouragingly. 'We are so jealous.'

Antoine was remembering the evening in the French committee, when I made them all magick restaurant tables. But he had absolutely no intention of letting the two journalists in on the secret. The waiter brought wine and filled the glasses. After he had gone, Antoine lowered his voice.

'Now, let's get down to business…'

After three hours, the party broke up, with Laura and Claire heading east to Brussels, and Antoine returning to Paris.

'Well, what are you going to write?' asked Claire.

'What do you think?' replied Laura. 'I'm going to write the lot. I'm glad I've got you as a witness. The boss is usually pretty good about these things, but this time…'

The two women laughed with a strange sense of elation.

'It could be the wine,' thought Claire, 'but this is one evening I won't forget.'

Next morning, Claire was wolfing down her scrambled eggs on toast, while reading the newspaper on the table in front of her. Laura was still getting dressed.

'It's here! Every word of it!' Claire shouted.

'No!' cried Laura, emerging in her slip, 'Give me that!.'

She snatched the newspaper and searched for the article. Eventually she found it... tucked away on page four:

'EU Committee Caught Short by Malicious Attacks!

'Brussels News has it on good authority that members of the EU Security and Defence committee have been kept in isolation, following attacks on their persons, causing maximum embarrassment and humiliation. Members of the committee have, reputedly, been forced to run to the toilet, their bladders and bowels suffering involuntary voiding, through criminal use of remotely controlled technologies that are normally used only in a hospital environment. Last night, committee members were seen leaving the Parliamentary building under full military escort. 'This cannot go on,' a source close to the committee told our reporter. 'Delegates say "We are being held hostage in our own homes".'

'I've already emailed a copy to Antoine,' said Laura excitedly.

Antoine clicked on his cell phone. He read the article attached to Laura's email.

'So, the cover-up goes on,' he thought, smiling sadly. 'How long will it be before we are allowed to speak freely?'

As a loyal French Parliamentary committee member, he

had signed his country's Official Secrets Act, and he wasn't about to risk everything for a few glasses of wine in pleasant company. Back in Brussels, Claire and Laura celebrated their modest 'scoop.' They had no idea how close they were to the story of the century, or how far away they were from ever discovering the truth.

VISIT TO IGRASHEL

Next day, I went to visit Linda, the head of the US Security and Intelligence committee. 'Where have you been?' she said, 'We've been waiting.'

The rest of the committee came in when they heard her talking to me.

'I'm really sorry,' I said. 'I had to arrange for the EU Defence and Security committee to go to Mars, and guess what? The EU military did the transportation this time.'

When they heard that, the US committee members began whooping and dancing round the room. 'The next step is to arrange a fact-finding visit for you on Planet Igrashel.'

'Oh yes,' said Linda. 'We've already been briefed on that by our military. We could go today, if they are ready for us on Igrashel.'

'Say, can you tell us about it?' asked a committee member.

'From what I've seen, it's like Arizona,' I said, 'A lot of desert sand.'

I thought that sounded quite inviting, but one of the delegates pulled a face.

'I don't want to go if it's like Arizona,' she said. 'I want a lush, tropical paradise.'

'Now, now,' said Linda, 'let's give Martha a chance to fix this up before deciding if anybody wants to opt out. It's not compulsory, remember.'

I thanked Linda for her support, and said I would try and fix things up as quickly as possible. Then I went straight over to Planet Igrashel, to the office of Dominic, the planet's deputy head. He was talking via videoconferencing facilities to Stephan, the head of the planet.

'Hi,' I said, 'I know you've been in discussion with the US Military about the visit of the US Security and Intelligence committee. When would it be convenient for the delegates to arrive?'

'Oh, we're ready anytime,' said Stephan.

'Where do you want me to take the delegates?' I asked.

'Well,' said Stephan smiling, 'we thought it would be best if you brought the delegates to the capital city, as that is quite different from our desert terrain, and is in fact, lush and tropical.'

It was obvious he had heard what the US delegates had been saying. 'Can you come over to my office for a moment?' asked Stephan.

I went to Stephan's video conference room, which was large enough to hold forty people easily. 'Bring them in here,' said Stephan.

I went back to the US committee room.

'I just spoke to the head of planet Igrashel,' I said. 'They are ready to go. And by the way, you are invited to their capital city, which is lush and tropical.'

The delegates quickly gathered together, expecting me to lift them up, and I was just about to do that, when I felt myself disconnected from the group environment. As I watched, the US Military took over, and transported the group straight into Stephan's teleconference room.

'No need to worry about collecting them, Martha,' said

the official on duty in the US committee lounge. 'We'll do that.'

'Great!' I thought. 'That's what we want to hear.'

I decided to keep an eye on the US group for a few moments, just to make sure that everything was going all right. As I watched, Stephan welcomed the group, and invited them to take a short tour of the city, starting with a panoramic walk round the glass walls on the top floor of the building he worked in. The group left his office, and started to walk round the glass walls. Outside, the sun was blazing down on a city of beige flat-roofed buildings arranged in terraces down steep hills. Tall trees stood behind the city, with long, trailing branches. Ferns and lush grass covered the low slopes of the mountains behind.

After walking round the building, the delegates stood at the top of an airlock, which took them, one after another, down what looked like a fairground helter-skelter ride, but in slow time. They descended safely inside a magnetic field, down to ground level. Once you were on the helter-skelter, you weighed less and floated down it, not touching the sides. Outside the air was warm with a slight breeze, which ruffled the plants and flowers in ornamental gardens. It looked like the ideal trip the US delegates had been hoping for.

I now had to arrange the last fact-finding visit for the UK committee, so I went to Howard's room to check that his group still wanted to go.

'Oh yes, of course we want to go,' said Howard.

'You could go to Planet Igrashel, but not today,' I said, 'as the US committee are there at the moment.'

'If you've no objection,' said Howard's duty officer, 'there is another planet in the Arturus group, called Defearra, which you could visit today. And we could transport you both ways. That would mean that between them the groups had seen three different planets — Mars, Igrashel and Defearra, which would give you a broader view of how things are.'

'Oh, fine, fine,' said Howard. 'If you have it all arranged, why don't we go there?'

He went to alert the rest of his group. They were all keen to go, and the UK Military soon assembled a "beaming-up" connection and transported them straight to Defearra. I was again disconnected while the process was going on, but I followed them up there, to make sure that arrangements were in place to receive the Brits.

Defearra's main city had glass buildings and was set at the bottom of a deep ravine with sharp sides. The valley was covered with tall trees. They didn't have leaves, but they had succulent pine needles hanging from every branch. The air was warm and humid, like Miami, and it rained every night. The Brits were welcomed by the head of Defearra, and ushered into a pleasant garden.

There was a soft, high-pitched background noise, like the sound of thousands of birds. But not a bird was in sight. One of the hosts put his hand out into the air, and as if from nowhere, he caught a bird. It was an inch long, green with a red head. Soon we got used to the noise, and it seemed like nothing more than cicadas.

In the garden, the group were served ice-cream sundaes. The Brits offered to make their hosts magick food tables, only to find that having gone Green, the people on Defearra were using similar tables to make the ice-creams. I noticed a very tall plant in the flowerbeds. It was eight feet tall and had a thin stem, with a deep, violet-coloured flower on the top, about two feet wide, which looked like a poppy.

I left the Brits taking a tour of the gardens.

'Well, that is that,' I thought. 'There is no need for my courier duties any more and I can leave it to the military.'

The principle had been established. Earth's peoples could travel to planets in space, and the process would now be subject to normal checks carried out by elected representatives.

ONE HUNDRED AND TEN YEARS AHEAD

Next day, I went to visit Linda, the head of the US committee. She was in her office at her desk, writing a report on the visit to Igrashel.

'Hi, did everything go all right?' I asked.

'Oh, sure,' said Linda. 'It was a dream. What a lovely place! And Stephan was the perfect host. I'm just putting the finishing touches to my initial report on the visit, before passing it round the committee for comment.'

'You've worked so hard,' I said. 'What are the next steps?' Linda put down her pen, and sighed.

'Well, we have to hold hearings to get information from people involved in all aspects of the Space Programme, taking into account the views of experts and lobby groups. We may have to involve people from other committees, where there are overlapping responsibilities. Then we will need to consider what needs to change to make the Space Programme properly accountable. That would include a review of all the things that are currently secret, and how much of what is currently secret justifies that classification. And finally, we will submit a report to the Senate, setting out our proposals.'

'But will the Senate be able to discuss such matters openly?' I asked. Linda nodded.

'I know what you're thinking, and you're right. The whole

subject is too sensitive to go before the full Senate. It will have to be dealt with in private, by people with the right security clearance levels to examine it. That will prevent open publication of our report.'

'How long do you think it will take for you to do what you need to do?' I asked. Linda thought for a minute before answering. 'I reckon we're looking at two years,' she said. 'But don't worry, Martha, too many people have been into space, not only here in the States, but also in Europe. Things will not go back to how they were before. You just can't keep this kind of thing under wraps.'

Linda smiled.

'There is one thing you could do for me though.'

'What's that?' I asked.

'When we were on Mars, sitting in the bar, you talked about your journeys into the past.'

'Oh yes, I remember,' I said. *13

'Well,' said Linda, 'have you ever thought about going into the future?'

'Oh, no!' I replied.

'Why not?' asked Linda.

'The past has already happened from our perspective,' I said, 'but the future is not set in stone. We have free will, which means that things can change. You can't rely on findings based on what, from our perspective, hasn't happened yet.'

'OK, OK, I hear you,' said Linda, 'but I would be curious to know how long it takes for us to get all this out into the open, and how it's going to happen.'

'Leave it with me, Linda,' I said, and wishing her good luck with her report, I left her to it. 'Well,' I thought, 'I suppose it's worth a try, but I don't have high expectations from this.'

I set aside time when I would not be disturbed, and tuning into the universal computer, I asked to see how the outcome of the reports would go, and when the Senate committee findings would be published.

Immediately, I was in a large room with soft, thick carpets, covered with patterns of flowers and leaves in warm colours. Fine wood panelling contrasted with the sunlight streaming in from large windows. The room had a spacious atmosphere, and there was a noticeable silence, as if the carpets and the panelling had muffled both speech and footfalls.

A man and woman appeared. The man looked to be in his early sixties and the woman in her late thirties. What was surprising was their clothing. They both wore clothes made from the same material, a light, grey-beige plaid with large black squares. It was the 'new black' for business wear. Then I heard a noise, and a door opened at the end of the room. Fifteen men and women wearing navy suits came out, talking quietly. I realised that we were outside the meeting room of a UK parliamentary committee.

More men and women gathered outside the committee room. Then a navy-suited woman came out.

'You can come in now,' she said, and the committee members trouped in, some wearing the grey-beige plaid, and some dressed in navy.

The committee members took their seats around an oval table. The chairwoman called the meeting to order.

'Thank you, everyone, for coming today, and thank you to everyone who has been in communication with me over the last few weeks. I think you have all studied copies of the draft report?'

Everyone murmured their approval and took out copies of

the report.

'As you will have seen from the draft,' continued the chairwoman, 'we have taken account of all your comments so far. Can I take it that you are now satisfied with the report as it stands?'

The committee members all indicated their agreement.

'And can I thank our staff for their hard work in helping to get us to this historic day, when we can finally produce our report,' said the deputy chairman.

'Now,' continued the chairwoman, 'I have been in contact with our friends in the States and in the EU, and we have agreed the procedures for co-ordinating the publication of all three committee reports.'

'I take it that they will all be published at the same time?' asked a committee member.

'Yes,' said the chairwoman. 'The US Senate committee invited us to co-ordinate publication dates and press notices. I understand that the US President, EU President and our Prime Minister are all going to make statements welcoming the reports, and that the timing of their statements will also be coordinated.'

At that moment, a tall, grey-suited man was ushered into the meeting room. His name was Matthew, and he was the cabinet minister with responsibility for Space Developments.

'Ah, Matthew, thank you for joining us,' said the chairwoman. 'We are looking forward to hearing about the arrangements for the publication of our report.'

'Yes,' said Matthew, 'I have just come from the Prime Minister's office, where I have had discussions about the timing of the announcements, and I can tell you that the provisional date set is in four weeks' time.'

Various members of the committee expressed their

interest at this.

'Our report will be ready for publication by then,' said the chairwoman, 'and we have the usual arrangements in place for sending advance copies to key people, and to the press, a few hours before the official statements are made.'

'And the PM's Office are in touch with the White House and the European Council President's Office to coordinate the timing of their speeches,' added Matthew.

'So far, so good,' I thought.

I "fast-forwarded" to see the historic announcements. On my mental screen I could see a packed auditorium. Then the US President walked forward to the microphone. The air was thick with camera flashes.

'It gives me the greatest pleasure to announce the publication of this historic report,' said the President. 'Not only does it represent the work of many men and women of our Senate, along with members of NASA, the space exploration community and the military, but also, the wider intergalactic community who, I hope, we will come to know better from now on. I am referring, of course, to representatives of our planet who have been in the forefront of space exploration, and have taken the human race onto other planets.'

The President paused for a moment, to give the photographers around the auditorium time to record this moment. A huge roar of applause could be heard, blending in with the sound of cameras.

'I know that for many of you, this announcement will come as no surprise,' the President continued. 'But it has taken many years for us to reach this stage. And let's not underestimate the effort that has gone into achieving this goal. heads of government around the world have worked for years in preparation for this moment.'

The President bent to pick up the report on the table in front of him. 'I want you to know that this report has my full backing, and I welcome all the recommendations in it. It is my hope that we will move forward as fast as possible to put those recommendations into practice.'

As the President waved the report in front of the cameras, I strained my eyes to see the date on it. And then I saw it! It read "2130".

'2130!' I was in shock. 'That's over a hundred years away. I can't believe it. I won't believe it!'

But there it was, and in the end, I had to believe it. With a heavy heart, I went back to Linda's office.

'Uh-oh, as bad as that, is it?' asked Linda, seeing my expression as I arrived.

I told her what I had seen, and she sat looking at the table for a minute, her head resting on her hands.

'Well, Martha, like you said, we have free will, which means that things can change. I'm not going to let this put me off. Thanks for taking the trouble to go there, but I'm still aiming for two years from now.'

'I really hope you and your team can fix it, Linda,' I said. 'Don't forget, if there's anything I can do, you know where to find me.'

I waved goodbye, but I felt low inside. Having lifted the lid on the future, there was more I wanted to know. I wasn't going to leave things looking like this. By the time I got home, I had already decided, I was going to travel three hundred years ahead. That way, I should have a clearer understanding what all this was leading up to, and be able to get a better perspective on things.

2320: THE GREAT EXODUS

Where to go first? I looked at a map of the world, with all the continents spread out before me. 'What about the Sahara?' I thought.

I took a deep breath and went straight into the year 2320… I searched for the familiar desert sand, but to my surprise, part of the Sahara was now a rather pleasant sea, stretching far inland, its green-blue waters lapping the golden shore. Thanks to global warming, and the melting of the ice-caps, the water level in the Mediterranean Sea had risen so much that it overflowed into North Africa. A few fishermen stood by the water, casting nets. Their catch was small, but the fish were large and healthy — sea bream by the look of it.

Moving on, I headed for the Antarctic. As expected, there was no ice left. Instead, there was a vast expanse of grey rock and mud, with snow on the highest peaks. High winds blasted the land mass, and penguins still gathered at the sea's edge. The sea was full of fish, enjoying the warmer currents, and the choppy seas were breached by the backs of whales arching out of the waters.

Many islands around the world had disappeared. Others had shrunk, including Japan, Cyprus and New Zealand. I looked in on the Solomon Islands, in the Pacific. Most of the islands had survived, but were smaller. There had been terrible cyclones which blew all the trees to the ground, and there was no sign of human life.

Turning my attention to the Middle East, I noticed that the Red Sea had bulged out into Egypt towards the north west, and that the Persian Gulf had spread into Saudi Arabia and Kuwait. The Black Sea now had a direct link to the Caspian Sea, and both had expanded into the surrounding territories. The mountains of Iran, which are currently dry and bare, had green foothills, with grass and small shrubs in sheltered areas, and trees were growing up the valleys.

The coastline of the Netherlands was unrecognisable. Towns and cities had withdrawn inland. Holiday destinations around the Mediterranean were significantly affected. All the beaches had disappeared. Cairo had flood problems, partly due to rising sea levels, and also because the Nile was spreading out more than ever at certain times of the year. The pyramids were not affected, but the land around them was covered with mud.

It was similar in the South of the United States. Well-known parts of New Orleans were no longer there, and where the Mississippi met the Gulf of Mexico, there was a vast expanse of still, brown water. I checked out the Statue of Liberty. It was encased in a huge, grey, protective shell, apart from the torch, which stood out on its own, covered in green moss, with ferns cascading from the top.

Finally, I turned to Time Square in New York. There was not a car in sight. It had become a pedestrian precinct, preserved for posterity. Some streets had disappeared, to be replaced by narrow alleys around the central area, with tourist shops and cafes. One or two people in waterproof jackets were making their way along the cobbled streets, the grey skies mirrored in rain puddles in uneven parts of the road.

Then I visited my home town, in the South of England, which is called Haslemere. My exploration started in an old churchyard. The grey stone church is already over one hundred years old at the time of writing, so in 2320 it would be four hundred years old.

As soon as I arrived, I got a shock. The church was completely covered in an outer shell of smooth red silicon material. The road by the railway station had been replaced by a dual carriageway which ran on each side of the railway track. The cars on the road were fully automatic. They looked like sports cars, low on the ground, but wider than our cars are. The back seats were designed like comfortable living rooms, with cupboards behind the front seats, for drinks, audio and video entertainment.

Two Irish terrorists, who were watching, noticed the car I was looking at. 'How do you think that's powered?' asked one.

'No petrol cap,' observed the other.

They looked at me expectantly. I am not a car driver, and really ignorant about car things. But I tuned into the universal computer system to see what, if anything, emerged. My eye was drawn to a skylight in the roof. The glass was reinforced, and there were tiny wires leading from the skylight to a box concealed in the roof. Sections of the chassis, which had a smooth, silicone finish, were also linked by wires to the ceiling box.

It appeared that the glass or silica material on the outside of the car, including the skylight, were able to convert daylight into electrical power. Small batteries in the ceiling box stored the power, which drove the vehicle.

The road carried on 'til it reached a huge roundabout at a town called Petersfield, with refreshment facilities and shopping malls leading off it. There was extensive car parking, with cars queuing for the car wash, to remove the mud and dust which fell from the sky. People in cars and shops wore transparent helmets and visors to protect themselves from air and dust pollution.

Across from the roundabout there were houses looking out on brown fields. It had rained recently, which was why the fields were brown. After the grass dried out, it became green again. The sky was completely covered with grey clouds.

'I must be unlucky with the weather,' I thought.

But it soon became clear that all this mud and rain was the result of global warming, and that there was one hundred percent cloud cover all over the world. I decided to visit the nearest house. A man wearing a helmet was working at a dining table, sorting out his bills and papers. I picked up his thoughts. 'Why must I do this? I have more than enough work to get on with.'

'How strange,' I thought. 'By now, it must be over two hundred years since the truth about space exploration was made public. So why are people still struggling to make a living on Earth?'

Taking a risk, I appeared before him.

'If I may interrupt you for a minute,' I said, 'why don't you go to another planet with a better life?' The man turned to me with a gasp of surprise.

'Where did you come from?' he stuttered.

'I'm from the past, from 2020. Please excuse me for arriving unannounced like this,' I said. 'I want to understand about the future.'

The man did not seem as surprised as I expected. By the year 2320, time travellers were more commonplace than they are now.

'You must be from the past, if you have to ask why I don't go to a planet with a better life,' he replied. 'We all want to leave, but you have to have a good job and be making money, to prove your suitability.'

'Do academic qualifications help?' I asked.

'Oh sure, sure,' the man gesticulated angrily with his arm, 'If you're a high-up person and can go to university, you can sail through. It's all right for them. But for the rest of us, we have to work at it, and it's hard.'

The man turned to me. His angry tone changed, and he sounded friendlier.

'I don't suppose you can help, can you?' he asked. 'Seeing that you've come all this way?'

For a moment, my mind froze. Then I did what I do when really stuck for a solution. I tuned into the universe and said, 'Wild card!'

Immediately, something heavy and dirty landed with a clunk on the table. 'What's that? Did you just do it?' asked the man.

'I asked the universe for help,' I admitted, 'but I don't know what that thing is.' The man examined it carefully.

'I know what that is,' he said. 'It's a type of glass signage. They were used for large motorways. Haven't seen anything like it for years. This gives me an idea.'

What is your work?' I asked.

'I'm a manufacturer. I invent things,' said the man. 'We need more signage on our roads these days, something that will resist our weather conditions, and I think this might be useful. It contains a water-resistant glass which displays lighted road signs effectively at night.'

The man turned away from me, absorbed in his thoughts about road signs.

I moved invisibly into the kitchen. A woman was preparing food. She had dark blonde, wavy hair and wore a long, A-line skirt and jumper. A strange contraption hung from the ceiling. It was a transparent tube, which turned into a ceiling rose at the top. At the bottom, four feet off the floor, was a transparent, plastic bubble, with a baby sitting in a purpose-built seat inside it. The baby could see everything round it and could make the bubble move from side to side.

As the woman cooked, she talked to the baby:

'Yes, yes. It's just coming,' she murmured, as she prepared the baby's meal.

Leaving the house, I headed for London. There were a lot of empty buildings, dating back to the nineteenth and twentieth centuries. Hardly anyone lived there now. The buildings could have been preserved as historic monuments, but no one wanted to spend money preserving them or even knocking them down. The city simply didn't have enough people to support itself any more.

It was great that we had got rid of inner-city overcrowding, but where had all the people gone? I tuned into the universal computer in search of an answer. Next moment I was in space outside the Earth. Our Earth was now surrounded by a number of well-equipped modern space stations. Space travel was available to everyone, but there were strict checks at space stations, with the back-up of military security.

People were flying up to the stations in space shuttles. There were different space stations for different planetary destinations. To board the space shuttles, they had to successfully complete a long Earth-based application process, like emigrating to Australia. On arrival at the space stations, they went through a series of final documentation and health checks to prove their entitlement and fitness to travel, and having passed those, they went to a waiting area, until their name was called.

I watched as a middle-aged woman was called to the departure gate. She showed her boarding pass and went through into another hall, where more people were waiting. She had no hand luggage and carried nothing in her pockets. The clothes she stood up in were now her only possessions. When her name was called, a female official in space uniform escorted her into a room where technicians were standing behind a transparent safety screen. On the other side of the screen was a clear cylinder, big enough to take a human body comfortably.

The woman was taken to the transparent cylinder, which had a security door. The door was opened, and the woman stood inside the cylinder, clutching her boarding pass. The security door was locked, and she was left alone inside. All space station personnel were on the other side of the safety screen. Then the cylinder began to glow with light, and as the light got brighter, the figure of the woman inside became hazy. And then she wasn't there. She had gone to the planet of her destination.

I followed the woman as she arrived on the other side. In the arrival room, an empty transparent tube started to flash. It glowed with light, and gradually, her shape reappeared. Then the light faded and you could see her, exactly as she looked before she left the space station. An official in protective clothing came forward and helped her out of the tube.

The woman stood there, with no luggage, no personal

possessions and nothing to remind her of her life on Earth. All she had was her boarding pass, which provided her identify details. And she had just gone Green, like all those who arrived on the new planet. Already, she was looking and feeling younger and fitter. She could hardly believe what was happening.

The official guided her out of the arrival area, towards the main reception hall. Behind the barriers in the hall, there were crowds of people, families, children, friends, all looking towards the arrival area, waiting for loved ones. There was a loud background hum, the sound of many people talking, and on the barriers, there were teddy bears, swathes of balloons, and banners saying, "Welcome home!" and, "Granny! We love you!"

The woman stood there in her beige mackintosh, looking bewildered. Her small, lonely figure was dwarfed by the size of the hall.

Then a young man let out a cry, 'Mummy! Mummy! Over here!'

A young man and woman rushed forward to the barrier, their arms outstretched. As the woman passed through the barrier gate, they hugged her, tears pouring down their faces. Smiling through her own tears, the woman bent to kiss her grandchildren. Then she and her family disappeared into the crowd, heading towards the large exit gates, through which the sun was pouring in. They finally emerged on the steps outside, to blue skies and wide, tree-lined streets. They did not have to fear the prospect of illness, old age or poverty. What would life be like now? It was a voyage of discovery for them all.

And this is where the missing millions from Earth had gone. In each country, it was the same. Those who could, went, and those that remained, prepared for the day when they too would go. Huge numbers of people had made this choice by the year 2320. And if by then global warming had messed up the weather in the rest of the world as much as it had done in the UK, who could blame them?

So finally, dear reader, what about you? What if your children had already chosen a new life in a new world? What if all your friends were leaving too? If you had seen what global warming was doing to the Earth, wouldn't you consider taking the short walk from the boarding gate to the beaming-up area? And if you already knew what life could be like on other planets, wouldn't you choose to make your home beneath a kinder sun? As unlikely as it may seem, future generations will make that choice, and some of them already have. Your descendants could be among them.

Annex 1: Dinosaur Time Travel

This is a record of my first visit into what we call the past. The method I use is exactly the same as for ordinary electromagnetic travel. I just tune into the frequency of where I want to go. But going into the past is trickier, as you need to find an object to tune into, which dates from the time you want to go back to.

For my first time-travel experiment I decided to see if it was possible to tune into the frequency of dinosaur bones, and arrive at a place where these animals were still alive and kicking. But first I needed to find dinosaur bones. I once visited the natural history museum in Ulan Batar, the capital of Mongolia, with its unforgettable dinosaur skeletons. In my mind I revisited the largest dinosaur room.

In front of me was the huge skeleton of a tyrannosaurus, it's backbone soared, arching towards a massive head, each jaw displaying a fearsome row of large teeth. I felt a longing to see the great beast alive, in its original environment.

Tuning into the frequency of the skeleton, I searched through time and space for a match. Everything went dark. In front of me, I could just see the glistening form of a huge animal. Its skin was nobbled like a crocodile, and its backbone now supported the heavy weight of muscles and flesh. It was lumbering forward, almost waddling, it's tail dragging in the sand. Around its feet there was a flurry of activity. Fish were flapping their tails from side to side in the wet sand.

Darkness began to fade into grey, as the first signs of dawn appeared. Grey shapes of tall tyrannosaurs came into view, their huge heads silhouetted against the cloudy sky. You could not see their teeth now, and their large eyes looked anything but fierce. They shuffled calmly along the vast sandy beach towards a small cliff.

At the bottom of the cliff, the sea battered itself against the rocks. But where beach started, the rocks were replaced by mudflats. The tyrannosaurs positioned themselves against the side of the cliff, close to the beach and waited. I could hear the roar of the sea, the deafening ebb and flow of the tide, and the crashing of water on rocks, as the sea bubbled and frothed.

A large wave beat against the rocks, and as it did so, small fish spattered out over the mudflats. They had been catapulted forward by the force of the waves. The waves were stopped in their tracks by the rocks, but the fish continued to shoot forward.

There was a flat grey fish that looked like a ray, and several plump fish that looked good to eat. But the tyrannosaurs ignored them. They were waiting for something bigger, and soon their wait was over. As the powerful tide came in, the sea hurled against the rocks with increasing force. Larger grey and silver fish, a cross between tuna and porpoise, came shooting out of the waves and onto the mudflats.

The first dinosaur moved forward towards its prey. Then another and another. Soon, five tyrannosaurs were gorging themselves on the large fish, their bared teeth tearing into the flesh, ripping off the skin as they went. They raised their heads above the cliff, as they chewed on the chunks of fish, before swallowing them.

There was a strong breeze, and high in the sky above, angular birds with long beaks floated in the wind, their leathery wings stretched out like kites. When the wind dropped, they landed on the sand, some way off from the dinosaurs, and started feeding on the smaller fish thrown up by the angry sea.

My mind withdrew from the scene and I was back in the Mongolian museum. I moved into another room, where the giant pelvis of a brontosaurus was on show. Again, I tuned into its frequency, and as the museum faded before my eyes, I was back on the beach. But a lot had changed.

We were a long way from the sea, and green trees had begun to grow on the sandbanks and surrounding hills. It was like a mangrove swamp, except that the swamp had dried out leaving the trees behind. Along the edge of the trees, several enormous brown animals, were grazing. They had exceptionally long necks, which they used to reach the leaves on the tops of the tree canopies. Their heads were tiny in comparison to their bodies.

The brontosaurus nearest to me had a strong, thick skin, like an elephant, but not wrinkled. The animal's tail was fleshier than I had expected, and its huge back legs must have weighed a ton. In spite of this, the animal whipped the end of its tail around with ease. Its undercarriage sagged heavily, so that its stomach hung a few feet above the ground and swayed slightly as it walked.

It tried to reach the topmost leaves on a branch, but even with its long neck, it couldn't. It leaned its neck round the stem of the tree and bent it down, so that the leaves were nearer to the ground. At that moment, another brontosaurus cantered over and grabbed the leaves greedily, before it could get them. But there were enough leaves for everyone, as the mangrove forest extended for miles.

Eventually, the herd moved away from the trees, into a higher, sandy area surrounded by hills. The first animal sat its body down, and lay on its side, while its head and neck stayed in the air, chewing away. Other brontosauruses came and lay near it. They looked very strange with their bodies flat on the ground while their necks and heads stood up at an angle, enabling them to look at each other and communicate while lying down.

More brontosauruses moved down the hills, following small streams into sandy ravines, where bright-green plants with large spreading leaves had established themselves. The animals took a few bites out of these leaves, before joining the rest of the herd lying down. Perhaps the leaves helped with the digestion process.

I looked up at the clock in my room and noticed the time. It felt as if five minutes had passed, but the clock showed an hour and a half had gone by.

'Perhaps time travel had something to do with it,' I thought.

NOTES

Chapter 2: *1. Blue-tits — Unimportant low-grade people. The saying arose from the fact that low-level terrorists did not wear any protective underwear above the waste, so their upper bodies got cold and turned blue.

Chapter 2. *2. Based on scientific research into measurements of cosmic background radiation, all events in the universe could be recorded in radio waves. I found that cosmic radio waves could be interrogated like a huge data storage computer, using thought or ultrasound to access the system.

Chapter 2: *3. Video on Synthetic Telepathy

It is really worth searching the internet for a YouTube video of Dr Joseph Pompei of MadLabs — 'making his own private racket in the library,' because it demonstrates how synthetic telepathy works.

See also: 'Sound from Ultrasound,' subheading 'Audio Spotlight,' on Wikipedia. It describes how Dr F Joseph Pompei of MIT developed the technology.

Chapter 6: 4*. The space station did not beam Natt down to the US base, as Natt was not inside the station. He was on the roof. Instead, the station control team gave the US base Natt's co-ordinates, and the US military used a phased location transformation to bring him down.

That means they surrounded Natt in a force field, and

altered his electromagnetic location indicator so that it moved from where he was standing to the inside of the US base. To do this safely from the top of the space station, involved introducing a time delay, so that Natt went from A to B to C etc, but at a speed that his body could accept.

Chapter 8: *5. Angels use musical instrument as frequency-raising devices. For them, singing fulfils the same purpose.

Chapter 10. *6. Pronounced 'Ineeoo.'

Chapter 15: *7. I asked Treto what is meant by a 'high spirit.' Treto said that high spirits were not the same as higher humans. 'High spirits are like I am,' said Treto. Then pointing upwards and backwards, it added 'We are from beyond.' I took that to mean that higher spirits are from the formless realm. Treto confirmed this, saying that both it and the gatekeeper were high spirits.

Chapter 16: *8. How did fallen angles develop human genitals? I checked with Treto, and apparently, this happened when fallen angels 'mingled their essence with humans.' The closer fallen angels got to humans, the more they took on human characteristics.

Chapter 19: *9. I went to visit Rufusha, and asked if his scientists could help me identify the components of the rare earths. Rufusha kindly offered to analyse the rare earth biscuits for me and found that they contained Iridium and a substance called Pteriosophate, which is not found on Earth. Iridium is used in electronics. Apparently, Pteriosophate is used for the outside of satellites and space vehicles.

Chapter 28: *10. Originally, the Dark angels wore uniforms when interacting with low frequency beings, because they shone too brightly to be visible to lower life forms. But over time, the reason for the uniforms was forgotten.

Chapter 33: *11. Stephan said that the car was powered by nitrogen, which was extracted by an advanced process from the air.

Chapter 34. *12. Fazing — Attack with a microwave radiation beam directed at the head, intended to confuse the mind.

Chapter 36. *13. For details of my time-travel visit to see dinosaurs, see Annex 1.